Ty®
Plush Animals

**Secondary Market Price Guide
and Collector Handbook**

First Edition

Ty® Plush Animals

Front cover (left to right): "Iris™" – *Attic Treasures™*, "Sherbet™" – *Pillow Pals™*, "Erin™" – *Beanie Babies®*, "Twigs™" – *Teenie Beanie Babies™*, "Romeo™" – *Ty® Plush*
Back cover (top to bottom): "Bongo™" – *Beanie Babies®*, "Papa Pumpkin™" – *Ty® Plush*, "Meow™" – *Pillow Pals™*, "Henry™" – *Attic Treasures™*

Managing Editor:	Jeff Mahony	Art Director:	Joe T. Nguyen
	jeff@collectorspub.com		*joe@collectorspub.com*
Associate Editors:	Melissa A. Bennett	Production Supervisor:	Scott Sierakowski
	Jan Cronan	Staff Artists:	Lance Doyle
	Gia C. Manalio		Kimberly Eastman
Contributing Editor:	Mike Micciulla		Ryan Falis
Editorial Assistants:	Jennifer Filipek		David Ten Eyck
	K. Nicole LeGard		
	Ren Messina		
	Joan C. Wheal		
Research Assistant:	Steven Shinkaruk		

ISBN 1-888914-35-1

COLLECTORS' PUBLISHING CO., INC.
598 Pomeroy Avenue
Meriden, CT 06450
www.collectorspub.com

TABLE OF CONTENTS

TABLE OF CONTENTS

INTRODUCING THE COLLECTOR'S VALUE GUIDE™

*W*elcome to the first edition of the Collector's Value Guide™ to Ty® Plush Animals. Ty Inc. has been a well-known name among plush enthusiasts since its inception in 1986 and the company's plush animals have won over the "hearts" of collectors everywhere! Our Collector's Value Guide™ is the "at your fingertips" reference you'll come to rely upon for information about Ty's popular collectibles. Easy-to-use and full of fun and informative sections, this comprehensive guide will assist you in building your collection.

EVERYTHING YOU NEED TO KNOW!

Throughout this guide, you'll find a wealth of information on Ty collectibles, including an extensive overview of the line, spotlights on all of the 1998 releases and retirements and the top five most valuable listings for each collection.

KEEP TRACK OF YOUR COLLECTION!

With full-color photos and lots of valuable information, the Value Guide is the resource that collectors have been waiting for! This section features all of the Ty plush animals ever released, including *Attic Treasures*™, *Beanie Babies*®, *Teenie Beanie Babies*™, *Pillow Pals*™ and *Ty® Plush*. Each piece is listed with information such as style number, issue year, status (current or retired) and 1998 secondary market value.

PLUS MORE!

Next, you can find out how to shop the secondary market, learn about variations and tags and get tips on caring for and insuring your collection. Read on for a chance to test your Ty knowledge with our trivia quiz, a glossary of collecting terminology, an index by animal type (for the entire collection) and much, much more!

𝒯n 1986, H. Ty Warner established his Illinois-based toy company, Ty Inc., with a litter of long-haired, life-like cats and a couple of dogs, hoping to successfully break into the retail world of plush animals that included Dakin, Warner's former employer. Little did he imagine that Ty Inc. would become the multi-million-dollar corporate leader in the production of bean bag toys and would initiate an intense collecting craze for his creation, the *Beanie Babies*.

Ty Warner's phenomenal success did not come immediately, however. His fledgling business enjoyed moderate success and, in 1989, Warner was looking forward to another profitable year. In the introductory letter to retailers from that year's catalog, Warner states his mission for the company with the words, "We are committed to be the best . . . The Very Best. A cut above the rest." It is quite obvious that the production of high quality, appealing products has helped Ty Inc. evolve into today's toy-making powerhouse.

By 1992, over 100 different styles and sizes of *Ty Plush* animals were available to selected retail and gift shops across the country. In 1993, in an effort to appeal to collectors and expand the line, Warner introduced the *The Attic Treasures Collection*™. Then, with the 1994 debut of *The Beanie Babies Collection*®, consisting of bean bag toys for children, and in 1995, the introduction of larger, baby-proof plush animals known as *The Pillow Pals Collection*™, it seemed that Ty was trying to provide "something for everyone." To continue this effort, Ty authorized McDonald's fast-food restaurants to produce and distribute miniature *Teenie Beanie Babies* in 1997 and 1998.

While many collectors may be most familiar with the *Beanie Babies*, they are just one branch of an extensive Ty family tree. In fact, over 600 plush animals have been produced by the company over the past twelve years. The sheer number of these cuddly creatures warrants a closer examination of their roots. Let's begin with a look at the old-fashioned and nostalgic . . .

TREASURES FROM THE ATTIC

Introduced in 1993, *The Attic Treasures Collection* first included twelve fully jointed bears and rabbits that were between 6 and 12 inches tall and had the style of the older, humpbacked, gangly-limbed teddy bears of the past. While most of the other Ty plush animals are naturally poseable due to the weighted bean filling in their extremities and tushes, the critters in this collection are fully jointed at their shoulders, hips and neck to offer additional posing options.

Up until 1993, the individual designers of Ty plush animals weren't named in catalogs or on tags, with most or all of the plush animals having presumably been designed by Ty Warner himself. To give his *Attic Treasures* a new look, Warner recruited Linda Harris and Ruth Fraser, renowned Canadian teddy bear artists, to provide original designs in addition to his own contributions. Over the next several years, Warner added two more artists to his creative team, Nola Hart and Anne Nickles. Warner gave credit to these artists by printing their signatures on their creations' swing tags.

Throughout its lifetime, *The Attic Treasures Collection* has undergone a number of changes. In 1995, its name was changed to "Ty Collectibles." The following year, some of the Attic bears and friends who initially wore simple neck ribbons opted to don an assortment of sweaters and overalls. Over the next few years, their closet expanded to include dresses, velour bloomers and even a fleece vest for "Morgan" the monkey! The collection's name reverted back to its original *Attic Treasures* moniker in 1998.

These plush reminders of the past have grown to number nearly 100 different styles of bears, bunnies, cats, dogs and occasional appearances from other species. With about half of these styles retired from production and Ty's recent trend of limiting shipments of pieces to retailers, *The Attic Treasures Collection* is becoming much more collectible.

HERE COME THE BEANIE BABIES®

At a Chicago area trade fair in late 1993, Ty Inc. introduced a line of bean bag animals that would soon become the hottest craze in the collectible market. The "Original Nine" *Beanie Babies* – "Splash," "Flash," "Legs," "Patti," "Pinchers," "Squealer," "Cubbie," "Chocolate" and "Spot" – were featured in the 1994 Ty catalog and sold at small retail gift shops in the Chicago area. The affordable $5 price tag on these approximately 10" critters provided just about everyone with the opportunity to start a plush animal collection with personality! Kids could eventually choose from a representation of many animals, including the common cat or everyday dog to the rare razorback or elusive iguana. These bags of beans are tiny and unassuming but have a charm that is absolutely impossible to ignore.

In the spring of 1997, Ty began a collaboration with a number of professional sporting leagues involving *Beanie Babies* giveaways in an effort to increase attendance at selected games.

A friend to many. A legend to all
The most popular figure in all of baseball
Crowds would cheer when hearing his name
Without you Harry, it won't be the same

In memory of Harry Caray
Ty presents Daisy™
at Wrigley Field
May 3, 1998

Consequently, the *Beanie Babies* given away during these popular promotions are also becoming coveted for their special commemorative cards.

The formation of the Beanie Babies® Official Club in 1998 was a result of Ty Inc. working in conjunction with the promotions company, Cyrk Inc. The $10 membership kit includes a variety of *Beanie Babies* materials, including stickers and a poster, and the opportunity to purchase the exclusive "Clubby" bear, who instantly became a star when he made his July 9, 1998 debut on national television's "Today" show.

In four short years, there have been over 150 different *Beanie Babies* designs produced by Ty. The overwhelming demand for some of the many retired versions and rare variations has resulted in an extraordinarily strong secondary market value for these hard-to-find *Beanie Babies*. Almost 60 designs are currently available in stores, but even these do not sit on the store shelves very long.

Much of the *Beanie Babies* phenomenon has been fueled by the Internet. At any time of day, collectors can log onto Ty's own site (www.ty.com) for up-to-date data on the entire

IT'S A WILD AND WONDERFUL WORLD

A family affair. *Attic Treasures* designer Nola Hart is the daughter of teddy bear designer Ruth Fraser.

Historical *Beanie Babies*. On September 13, 1998, Chicago Cubs slugger Sammy Sosa passed Babe Ruth and Roger Maris in the chase for baseball's single season home run record with his 61st and 62nd home runs on a special "*Beanie Babies* Day" where "Gracie" was given away.

Through the secret door. Ty Warner is a very private person and even his corporate headquarters is testimony to this. The front door is not marked with a number and there is no sign on the building's face.

Can't we all just get along? Brawls have broken out in neighborhood stores among eager *Beanie Babies* enthusiasts, searching for those hard-to-find critters.

A "Ty-Riffic" place to shop. At Chicago's O'Hare Airport, Ty Inc. authorized WH Smith to open "Ty-Riffic," a shop which sells only Ty products. On display, you can find a variety of prototypes for all the lines.

line, as well as countless other sites devoted to conversation, gossip, rumors and trading.

A Not-So-Teenie Story

In April of 1997, Ty authorized McDonald's – the fast-food conglomerate and part-time toy distributor – to produce ten small replicas of *Beanie Babies* called *Teenie Beanie Babies* which were distributed with the McDonald's Happy Meals. In fact, this promotion became a collectible feeding frenzy beyond belief. Television news shows aired reports of people loading trunk fulls of Happy Meals into their cars and web sites began selling promotional posters and buttons worn by employees during the event.

The immense popularity of the 1997 *Teenie Beanie Babies* promotion prompted Ty and McDonald's to team up once again for a promotion in May 1998 which offered 12 new mini counterparts to their larger *Beanie Babies* siblings. And once again, Happy Meals became a very popular mealtime request – so popular that once again they sold out within a month, leaving many collectors hungry.

New Pals On The Block

Ty also produces the *Pillow Pals*, which are polyester-filled, machine washable, animal-shaped pillows designed especially for infants. These kid-friendly animals are made with embroidered eyes and noses that cannot be removed easily by little fingers or mouths. The first seven animals introduced in 1995 were the bears, "Snuggy" and "Huggy," "Woof" the dog, "Snap" the turtle, "Ribbit" the frog, "Oink" the pig and a cow named "Moo."

If these critters give you a sense of déjà vu, it is no wonder as many of them have been designed to mirror some of their *Beanie Babies* cousins. For example, "Tubby" looks a great deal like "Happy" and "Red"' bears a striking resemblance to "Snort." Perhaps the next Ty line collection to jump on the collectible bandwagon, *Pillow Pals* is making even the youngest of collectors true Ty fans.

THE PLUSH PARTY OF 300+

The plush animals that started it all for Ty were four longhaired Himalayan cats introduced in 1986, which retailed for around $25. The early collection included a variety of other furry cats and three sizes of "Schnapps," the white dog. Over the years, this category of *Ty Plush* has ballooned to more than 300 items with about 80% of them having been sent to the Ty retirement home (though most were taken out of production before Ty began to use the official "retirement" term). This large assortment of animals has been divided into five basic groups which will make your plush hunt much more manageable.

BEARS: These bruins make up the largest section of plush – over one third of the *Ty Plush* animals are teddies and their related bear relatives.

CATS: Since 1986, tabbies, calicos, Persians and others have joined the Himalayans in this family of felines.

DOGS: These "ruff" types are a popular section for collectors with its wide variety of breeds and sizes.

COUNTRY: This group features selections from the country, including lambs and bunnies, pigs and cows from the farm and even a mystical unicorn.

WILDLIFE: Collectors can also go "wild" choosing from this rowdy group which includes apes, a moose and a seal.

While all of these toys feature the famous Ty "poseability," a few of them are also jointed and there are some pieces that are absolutely gigantic in size! Imagine the delight (and surprise!) in a child's eyes upon seeing a four-foot tall "Jumbo George" gorilla or a 50 inch "Papa Rumples" bear for the first time!

Because the *Ty Plush* collection was "born" before anyone realized the importance of the red Ty swing tags, it is very rare to discover an older toy from this line with tags in pristine condition. Consider it your lucky day if you happen to do so!

Ty® Takes Over The World

The phenomenon of the *Beanie Babies* is starting to carry over into the entire line of Ty plush animals. Where and when will this all end? And do we really want it to end? Of course not!!

Not only do these lovable creatures have plenty to offer with a soft cuddle and a pair of sympathetic eyes, they also take on the collectible world with a great bit of amusement. Where else can you find a graceful ballerina who is also a hippopotamus? Or a platypus hanging out with a cheeseburger? And the fun doesn't stop there. The phrase, "What's in a name?" has special meaning among these furry pals. There are a couple of bears named "Eleanor" and "Theodore" and some bulldogs named "Winston" and "Churchill." "Ashes," "Cinders" and "Pepper" are all black labs and "Cinnamon," "Nutmeg" and "Honey" are just some of the flavorful bears that spice up the line.

The more we get involved with the "search and rescue" of these elusive and rare animals, the more fun we all have! With over 600 different plush animals to choose from, Ty Inc. is able to provide something to love for just about anyone!

PRODUCTION, PACKAGING AND PRICING

Each Ty plush animal is an individually hand-crafted item that is held to high standards in production and safety. All fabric and materials are non-allergenic, colorfast and non-flammable, paints are non-toxic, and only lock-washer eyes and noses are used. Every animal is sewn by hand and has handpainted eyes. They are poseable due to the weighted filling inside each plush animal and are individually groomed before being shipped to retailers around the country.

With the exception of the small plastic bags for the *Teenie Beanie Babies*, Ty plush animals are sold without a protective bag or box. However, each animal does come with an identifying Ty swing tag and tush tag.

Retail pricing for Ty products range from the suggested $5-$7 price tag for *Beanie Babies* to around $250 for the currently available four-foot *Ty Plush* gorilla named "Jumbo George."

A total of 95 animals have joined the Ty family in 1998 among the five different collections. Whether you like your plush animals with clothes or without, "teenie" or jumbo, wild or domesticated, there's a Ty plush animal out there for you.

ATTIC TREASURES™

Attic Treasures is a rapidly-growing collection with 27 new releases in 1998, 23 of which were released in January while four made their debut in May. You'd better act fast, because many of the 1998 releases have already been retired. Not included here is the mysterious "Tulip," a rabbit which was pictured in the 1998 Ty catalog. According to Ty, "Shelby" the rabbit was incorrectly identified as "Tulip" in the catalog and was not produced with that name. These new clothed and unclothed *Attic Treasures* animals will bring much personality into your collection.

Amethyst™ . . . A real gem is what this adorable cream cat is, dressed in her best purple velvet bloomers. With her long tail and short ears, "Amethyst" is sure to add a brilliant shine to your collection if you were lucky enough to get her before her July retirement.

Bearington™ . . . You won't be able to bear it if you missed the chance to add this adorable teddy to your collection. Sporting a huge black and tan plaid ribbon around his neck and wide, curious eyes, the recently retired "Bearington" is definitely one to seek out.

Bloom™ . . . Displaying her love of fresh veggies on her dress, "Bloom" is a fresh introduction to the market. Unfortunately, this hare's harvest season was short as she was retired in May.

Bluebeary™ . . . Don't let the name fool you – this bear is only blue in color. "Bluebeary" with his unique curly hair is a happy little bear, guaranteed to cheer up any lucky collector who sees him.

Bonnie™ . . . "Bonnie" is quite a unique chick. Wearing her favorite blue and white checkered bonnet and matching blue bow, and with her bright yellow feathers and orange beak, this little lady is chirping for attention!

Casanova™ . . . It will be love at first sight when you lay eyes on this cuddly "Casanova." He'll show his love for you with a big red heart right in the middle of his knit sweater.

Ebony™ . . . Don't worry about bad luck if this black kitty crosses your path – the only spell she'll cast on you is to bring her home. And "Ebony" will surely captivate you when you see her in the burgundy velvet romper she wore before retiring in July.

Eve™ . . . This dainty little lady adds an unique Victorian look to the *Attic Treasures* spring introductions. Her beautiful ivory-colored lace cape and colorful wreath of flowers on her head, as well as the innocent expression on her face, will remind collectors of a more elegant time gone by.

Gloria™ . . . Making her appearance in time for the July 4th holiday celebration, this bunny sparkles in the eyes of collectors. In her red, white and blue overalls, "Gloria" will be the pride of

your collection. However, she's hard to find as she was retired at the end of July!

Grace™ . . . With a graceful entrance, this hippo sashayed her way into the *Attic Treasures* spotlight. As "Grace" becomes the only ballerina among her *Attic Treasures* friends, she is sure to entertain them and collectors alike. "Grace" took her final bow in September when she was retired.

Grant™ . . . As "Grant" wears his pride of his country on his sweater and with a name shared with one of the country's most famous presidents, it's stars and stripes forever for this little bear. "Grant" was released in January, already revved up for America's birthday.

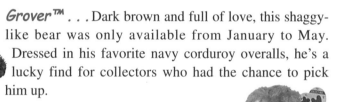

Grover™ . . . Dark brown and full of love, this shaggy-like bear was only available from January to May. Dressed in his favorite navy corduroy overalls, he's a lucky find for collectors who had the chance to pick him up.

Iris™ . . . This tan rabbit with long, floppy ears is one of several rabbits named for flowers to join *Attic Treasures* in 1998. With her namesake on her purple overalls, "Iris" brings a glimpse of spring into any collection.

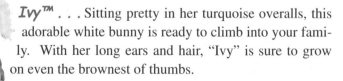

Ivy™ . . . Sitting pretty in her turquoise overalls, this adorable white bunny is ready to climb into your family. With her long ears and hair, "Ivy" is sure to grow on even the brownest of thumbs.

King™ . . . As "King" of the lily pads, this green frog is sure to become your next prince charming. Wearing a burgundy cape tied in front with a ribbon, he stands a regal 11 inches tall, replacing his other "King" amphibian friend who retired at 9 inches.

Montgomery™ . . . This moose is quite the talk of the town around his *Attic Treasures* friends as he is the first of his kind to join the line. In his safari vest, "Montgomery" came out of the woods for only a short time as he was retired in September.

Peppermint™ . . . This bright white bear is as sweet as her name implies. And she's definitely ready for the cold weather of winter – not only does she have a thick coat of fur helping her get by, she also has her favorite red scarf and hat.

Piccadilly™ . . . Dressed in a green and blue jester suit, with a red, Bozo-type nose, this bear would do back flips to win your heart. Once "Piccadilly" jokes his way into your home, he promises to make a serious impression on your collection.

Precious™ . . . This precious light brown cub is all set for naptime, wearing a diaper and a nightcap, with pillow close by. As one of the only "babies" in the *Attic Treasures*, this one is definitely *not* a sleeper! The quick retirement of "Precious" in September hopefully didn't catch too many collectors napping!

Rose™ . . . Even though this bunny has dark brown hair, with a name like "Rose," you know she has a bright and sunny heart. With those long, floppy ears and her salmon-colored overalls, she's a blooming addition to the bunch.

Samuel™ . . . Decked out in his Fourth of July holiday best, the spirited "Samuel" is looking rather spiffy. His outfit includes a navy blue top coat, with red and white striped pants and a matching top hat. You'll have a hard time finding any other bear with this much American pride.

Sara™ . . . This adorable white bunny is ready to listen to anything you have to say, with her long ears sitting high on her head. While everyone who sees "Sara" in her peach bloomers will want to take her home, her ears are all yours if you make her part of your collection.

Scotch™ . . . The perfect little Scotsman, "Scotch" is dressed up in his best plaid outfit. His light brown fur is the perfect complement to his plaid overalls and matching plaid hat. "Scotch" quickly marched back to the Highlands when he retired in July.

Scruffy™ . . . With his long, scruffy hair and ears, this pup's name says it all. "Scruffy" is quite an interesting dog, but you can see it in his eyes – he's more than willing to clean up his act if he can just have a spot in your heart!

Sidney™ . . . You're sure to be taken back in time when you see this little bunny. With her long ears sticking straight up, "Sidney" comes across as a very curious little hare. Strutting around in her burgundy bloomers, she's ready to take on your collection. "Sidney" is one of the many 1998 *Attic Treasures* releases to have already been retired.

Sire™ . . . He's the king of the jungle, and just loves to dress the part. "Sire" comes complete with a dark purple velvet cape and gold crown fit for a king. Let this now-retired roaring treasure reign over your collection!

Strawbunny™ . . . This cheerfully colorful bunny is ready to hop into the hearts of the collectors who see her. So don't let her sad eyes get you down – she's really in the pink!

BEANIE BABIES®

This section highlights the 27 *Beanie Babies* releases for 1998. Announced on the last day of 1997, 12 new designs kicked off the year in style, while 15 others joined the *Beanie Babies* wilderness by the end of May. As always, these exciting new releases are among the most coveted collectibles around!

Ants™ . . . Ants aren't the only things this long-nosed critter is looking for. What would really feed his hunger is a place in your loving home with all of his friends.

Britannia™ . . . As she is so adorable, it's not only die-hard *Beanie Babies* collectors who could be swayed to travel to Great Britain in search of this special bear.

Proudly displaying the flag of the United Kingdom on her chest, "Britannia" is exclusive to Great Britain and has become quite a catch for collectors in the United States.

Bruno™ . . . This terrier is not the brute his name implies. And as we all know, a dog is man's best friend and "Bruno" promises to be no less if you were able to chase him down before he retired in September.

Clubby™ . . . This bear has the most exciting position of all the *Beanie Babies*: he's the "Beanie Babies® Official Club™" bear. Released in honor of the first year of the club, this bright blue bear won't be found on any store shelves. "Clubby" can only be ordered by club members – giving you one more reason to join!

Early™ . . . As you know, the early bird catches the worm, and that's just how this robin got his name. It's easy to tell "Early" often gets the worm – his big red belly gives it away. So what are you waiting for? Now *you* have to be early and get this new release before your chance flies away.

Erin™ . . . Released in time to celebrate St. Patrick's Day, "Erin" is filled with lots of luck. With a bright green coat and a white clover on her chest, she promises to share her good fortune with you! Don't be surprised if you have to really search for this bear though – she's almost as hard to find as a pot of gold at the end of a rainbow!

Fetch™ . . . You won't want to miss the opportunity to "Fetch" a playful new dog. This adorable little pup is chasing after a collector to love.

Fortune™ . . . Feeling lucky? You will be if you find your "Fortune." This black and white panda hasn't made it to the endangered (or retired) list yet, but don't let that stop you from grabbing her from the shelves.

Gigi™ . . . This poodle is looking first class with her curly, black coat and red bows around her ears. "Gigi" is sure to love any home she joins, as long as she's "in the spotlight," able to show off her pristine look to all of her *Beanie Babies* friends!

Glory™ . . . Covered from head to toe with red and blue stars and topping it off with the American flag proudly displayed on her chest, "Glory" is spotted with patriotism. This celebratory bear, released in time for Independence Day, takes pride in being the most patriotic of all her friends!

Hissy™ . . . This snake came out of winter hiding early this year, coiled and ready to strike at your heart. But you have nothing to worry about because, unlike any other snake you'll come across, "Hissy" is full of love, not venom.

Iggy™ . . . "Iggy" decided to trade in his lonely life in the hot desert for some cool friends. He found more than he imagined – now he needs you to bring him home so he can join them! "Iggy" has played tricks on collectors everywhere, as most have appeared with "Rainbow" swing and tush tags.

Jabber™ . . . Talk, talk, talk . . . that's all this colorful parrot wants to do. Likely to talk his way right into your heart (and home), "Jabber" is sure to make a vibrant addition to your collection.

Jake™ . . . This new feathered friend is the second duck (after "Quackers") to wade into the *Beanie Babies* flock, leaving his pond behind to find a place in your home. With his wings spread, "Jake" promises to fly into your heart and stay forever.

Kuku™ . . . Don't let the name fool you – this "Kuku" really is a smart one. He'll chirp all day long until he convinces you to take him home and once he's there, he'll soar right into your heart.

Pounce™ . . . This frisky feline is jumping at the chance to be a part of the *Beanie Babies* phenomenon. With his dark brown fur and white paws, "Pounce" is ready to make the leap from store shelves to your collection.

Prance™ . . . Another cat has clawed its way into the 1998 releases, although a bit more gracefully. "Prance" is an adorable cat with dark stripes, "puurrfect" for cuddling up to the rest of your collection.

Puffer™ . . . This puffin took a break from the cold of the Arctic to find the warmth of your home. With her big orange-and-yellow beak and black-and-white body, "Puffin" made quite a splash in many collections before retiring in September.

Rainbow™ . . . This colorful chameleon couldn't decide on what color he liked best, so he chose all of them! It doesn't matter either because, as you will soon find out, he has nothing to hide from; in fact, he wants you to notice him and take him home. Many of the first chameleons shipped to stores had incorrect "Iggy" swing and tush tags attached. Adding more intrigue to this deceptive fellow, he can also be found with or without a tongue!

Rocket™ . . . As one of several birds soaring onto the list of new releases this spring, "Rocket" is sure to hit a home run with collectors. With his bright blue and white color, he's a sure hit for his species.

Smoochy™ . . . You won't find your prince by kissing this frog, but your collection could leap forward with the addition of "Smoochy." This green and yellow frog hopped into the line this year filled with lots of, you guessed it, kisses for all of his collectors!

Spunky™ . . . This cocker spaniel's name is true to his nature. "Spunky" joined his Ty friends early in the year and is eager to jump into your collection.

And don't worry about training this little guy. He's sure to do anything to make you happy.

Stinger™ . . . The only thing missing from this guy is his stinger . . . and that's a good thing! Besides, "Stinger" would rather spend time with you – and the rest of his Ty friends – than crawl around in the hot sun looking for a fight.

Stretch™ . . . You'll need lots of room for this gal so she can "Stretch" those long legs of hers. This brown and white ostrich may look like she'll run for miles, but once she makes it to your collection, she's there to stay!

Tracker™ . . . Once he's on a scent, this determined basset hound is not about to stop the hunt. Since his release this spring, "Tracker" has been looking for nothing but a good home. And either with the help of his sensitive nose, or those sad puppy dog eyes, he's sure to find his way into your collection.

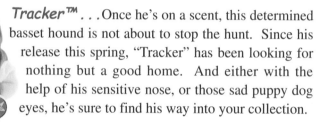

Whisper™ . . . Shhhh! This baby fawn needs her peace and quiet so she can grow up to be a "deer" to your collection. Very elegant indeed, "Whisper" is a quiet animal ready to make a loud entrance into your heart.

Wise™ . . . This brainy owl looks very scholastic in the cap he sports on his head. Released right at the end of graduation season, "Wise" is constantly striving to be number one, not only in the "Class Of '98," but also in your collection!

TEENIE BEANIE BABIES™

Just when you thought that the hunger for *Beanie Babies* couldn't get any bigger, it did! McDonald's restaurants returned this year to the *Beanie Babies* scene with another sizzling spring release of the much anticipated *Teenie Beanie Babies*.

In 1997, the ever-popular fast-food chain teamed up with Ty for a special promotion, selling "teenie" versions of ten *Beanie Babies*. The little critters could only be purchased at the restaurants and the promotion was an astronomical success. In 1998, the event was twice the size and included 12 Teenies. The promotion, which began May 22, was once again successful, feeding the appetites of millions of Beanie collectors across the country.

The sold-out heroes of the 1998 promotion were "Bones" the dog, "Bongo" the monkey, "Doby" the doberman, "Happy" the hippo, "Inch" the inchworm, "Mel" the koala, "Peanut" the elephant, "Pinchers" the lobster, "Scoop" the pelican, "Twigs" the giraffe, "Waddle" the penguin and "Zip" the cat.

PILLOW PALS™

There were nine fluffy critters to join the *Pillow Pals* family this year. Seven of these playful pals made their debut in January, while "Paddles" and "Sherbet" joined them in May.

Clover™ . . . This cute little bunny is better than any four leaf clover for bringing love and happiness into any collection. Decked out with a peach-colored ribbon around her neck, "Clover" is a lucky find.

Foxy™ . . . With what appears to be a smile on his face and the slick brown bow tied around his neck, one can only wonder what this sly little guy is up to. Not to worry though – the only thing he wants to do is fox trot into your heart.

Glide™ . . . Gliding into 1998 in a most graceful way is one of the first water animals of the *Pillow Pals* collection. "Glide" is an adorable porpoise ready to take you on an unforgettable water journey. And she is ready to please and will surely jump through a few hoops to become part of your collection.

Paddles™ . . . This adorable platypus made her debut as one of only two *Pillow Pals* released this spring. Her bright magenta coloring and yellow webbed feet will make it easy for her to paddle her way into your heart.

Red™ . . . This Pillow Pal is ready to charge his way into your home. While "Red" likes to tease a little bit, don't mistake this guy for a bully . . . the only bullying he's going to do is to bully you into taking him home.

Sherbet™ . . . With a name like "Sherbet," you're guaranteed a cool animal. This tie-dyed treat has attracted a lot of attention since being released this spring.

WHAT'S NEW FOR TY® PLUSH ANIMALS

Spotty™ . . . Yes, you *are* seeing spots! But it's okay because they're on one of the most adorable of the *Pillow Pals* released so far! "Spotty" the dal-matian is dog-gone adorable with his red rib-bon around his neck and, of course, those big black ears!

Swinger™ . . . Monkey see, monkey do! That's what "Swinger" is all about. He sees his fellow *Pillow Pals* leaving the stores and immediately wants to join them. Despite his name, "Swinger" promises to stay put once he's made it into your home.

Tide™ . . . This giant whale joins "Glide" the porpoise this season with a huge splash. Searching high and low for a good home, "Tide" is sure to drench you with love.

TY® PLUSH

This section highlights the 19 new animals to join the *Ty Plush* wilderness this year. Most of these crea-tures joined the family in January, with only three wait-ing until May to make their debut.

BEARS

Baby Paws™ . . . As the tiniest of his family, this unforgettable white bear cub will paw his way into your heart. "Baby Paws" loves to show off what his family's named for – his padded paws!

Bamboo™ . . . This guy would love the captivity of your home so you better catch this black and white

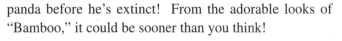

panda before he's extinct! From the adorable looks of "Bamboo," it could be sooner than you think!

Forest™ . . . There's no need to be afraid – there's nothing but love growing in this "Forest." So you'd better hike on over to the store because it will be hard to bear it if you don't add this grizzly guy to your collection.

Large Paws™ . . . This big white bear is the Grand'paw' of "Baby Paws" . . . and he's just as lovable. His brilliant white fur and deep black eyes are great complements to his most prominent feature: his paws!

Magee™ . . . "Magee" has come out of hibernation to join the 1998 spring introductions as a brown teddy bear with a gold ribbon. A little sleepy from her long winter's nap, she'll be bursting with energy when you bring her home to play with the rest of her *Ty Plush* friends in your collection.

Paws™ . . . In between the other two "Paws," this medium-sized "Paws" doesn't have to worry about the middle child syndrome. This bear is just as adorable as the rest of his family and collectors will not pause to think twice before taking him home.

Romeo™ . . . There's no need to look any further for true love – this adorable white bear with a ribbon around his neck is sure to steal your heart . . . or give you his. As he sits holding a big red heart in his paws, he wonders if you will be his next Juliet. "Romeo" appeared in stores with a special purple ribbon for Mother's Day, but later changed his outfit to a gold "I Love You" ribbon.

CATS

Angel™ . . . This adorable longhaired cat is heaven-sent. With her white coat and pretty pink ribbon around her neck, "Angel" will bring an angelic touch to any collection.

Boots™ . . . With her four white boots on her feet, this little kitty is made for walking. Dressed for a night out on the town, her "outfit" is topped off with a red bow tied around her neck. But don't worry about this kitty straying, the only place she really wants to walk to is your home.

Licorice™ . . . This solid black cat is as sweet as her name. And with her long black hair, puffy tail and bright red bow tied around her neck, "Licorice" is eye candy for anyone who sees her.

Spice™ . . . This little cat is adding a touch of "Spice" to the 1998 recipe for releases. You'll need just a dab of her love to know that she really cares. With a royal blue bow tied around her neck, this cinnamon-colored kitty is just the right ingredient for your collection.

DOGS

Ace™ . . . This playful pooch could be your lucky "Ace." When you see this little puppy covered in black spots from nose to tail, it will be impossible to keep a straight poker face.

Sherlock™ . . . It's no mystery why everyone falls in love with "Sherlock" – he knows the solution to finding his way into your heart. After all, who could resist after seeing his sad little puppy dog eyes?

Sunny™ . . . "Sunny" comes into the 1998 line, shining some light on why people love *Ty Plush* so much. This puppy is a soft beige color, with the sweetest puppy dog eyes you'll ever see!

COUNTRY

Bows™ . . . Hopping around in the country all day is hard work for the little rabbit "Bows." Once he gets to rest in your home, he'll be much happier!

Buttons™ . . . "Buttons" hops down the bunny trail alongside his friend "Bows." This bunny with long white ears is ready to call your home his own.

Lovie™ . . . She's a real "lovie-dovie" of a lamb, with her cream fur and lavender ribbon. You can tell just by looking that she's extremely gentle. Her love is endless, unlike her availability – "Lovie" was retired in May.

WILDLIFE

Cha Cha™ . . . Wanna dance? This brown, hairy monkey cha-chas his way right into the 1998 spring season. If you promise to take him home, he promises not to step on your toes.

WHAT'S NEW FOR TY® PLUSH ANIMALS

Misty™ . . . Don't be surprised to see yourself misty-eyed over this adorable creature. Just like all baby seals, "Misty" has bright white fur that is sure to get your seal of approval.

WEB WORDS FROM THE "WISE™"

Kids and collectors everywhere have become hooked on Ty's fun and creative web site (www.ty.com). One of the popular features of the site is the Info Beanie Diary. A different Beanie Baby is voted in as "Info Beanie" each month. In September 1998, "Wise" the owl quickly stumbled onto a mystery of some very elusive creatures. What was the big thing that was happening at Ty headquarters? Here's a quick rundown of some curious clues:

September 2: "Wise" overhears his friends at Ty saying, "I can't wait to see them . . . I wish we didn't have to wait so long though."

September 8: "Wise" gets his wings on an "IMPORTANT, SPECIAL PROJECT" document but is unable to decipher the cursive writing. He then sees a strange creature lurking in the hallways at Ty and exclaims, "It was like nothing I had ever seen before! It certainly wasn't one of the current Beanies nor was it an Attic Treasure or a Pillow Pal."

September 10: "Tracker" the basset hound discovers "a new scent. Nothing like he had ever smelled before. He said it definitely wasn't a Beanie!"

September 11: "Wise" discovers a clump of fur which he "had never seen or felt anything like it."

September 12: "Wise" and "Batty" discover unusual paw prints in the kitchen.

September 16: The mystery creatures sneak onto the Ty web site and add an entry into the diary saying, "Hi. How are you? . . . Don't tell him we were here. OK?"

September 20: "Wise" receives a letter from his secret friends which states, "Pretty soon we will be introduced to you and we'll have a big party.""

Are there new friends joining the Ty plush animals family? Stay tuned to the Ty web site to find out!

www.ty.com

*J*t has been an exciting year for collectors of *Beanie Babies* with the formation of the first-ever collectors' club for a Ty plush animal line. In early January 1998, Ty announced its partnership with the Massachusetts-based marketing company, Cyrk, Inc. and their plans to develop the Beanie Babies® Official Club and design the Official Club Kit. These kits, available for a suggested retail price of $10, have been for sale at authorized Ty retailers since March. The membership kit includes an official membership card, over 100 *Beanie Babies* stickers, a checklist, a newsletter, club membership certificate mail-in card, a doorknob sign and a 33" x 50" poster.

OFFICIAL CLUB ADDRESS

Beanie Babies® Official Club™
P.O. Box 842026
Dallas, TX 75284-2026

When members receive the Certificate of Club Membership from Ty, they will find a reply card which provides information on "Clubby," a royal blue bear with a tie-dye ribbon and a club logo "pin" on his chest. "Clubby" was introduced to Katie Couric and the rest of the country in July on the "Today" show, a nationally televised morning news program. This "members only" bear is available by mail order for $5.99 plus applicable sales and shipping charges from the Beanie Babies Official Club address in Dallas, Texas. "Clubby" began shipping to club members in September.

Collectors who want *every Beanie Babies* design for their collection should join the club today, because there are sure to be more special pieces to come!

*𝒯*n 1998, Ty Inc. retired a total of 86 pieces, including 27 *Attic Treasures*, 40 *Beanie Babies*, the entire 12 *Teenie Beanie Babies* from the 1998 McDonald's promotion, five *Pillow Pals* and two *Ty Plush*. Most announcements are made on the Ty web site while others (such as those in the *Teenie Beanie Babies* and *Ty Plush* collections) are usually not formally announced. Here's a list of those pieces that were honored with retirement through September 1998 with their animal type, style number and issue year.

1998 ATTIC TREASURES™ RETIREMENTS

Abby™ (bear, #6027, 1995)
Amethyst™ (cat, #6131, 1998)
Bearington™ (bear, #6102, 1998)
Bloom™ (rabbit, #6122, 1998)
Chelsea™ (bear, #6070, 1996)
Christopher™ (bear, #6071, 1996)

Dickens™ (bear, #6038, 1996)
Ebony™ (cat, #6130, 1998)
Fraser™ (bear, #6010, 1993)
Gloria™ (rabbit, #6123, 1998)
Grace™ (hippo, #6142, 1998)

Grover™ (bear, #6100, 1998)
King™ (frog, #6140, 1998)
Lilly™ (lamb, #6037, 1995)
Madison™ (cow, #6035, 1995)

1998 ATTIC TREASURES™ RETIREMENTS, CONT.

Mason™ (bear, #6020, 1995)
Montgomery™ (moose, #6143, 1998)
Morgan™ (monkey, #6018, 1994)
Nicholas™ (bear, #6015, 1994)
Oscar™ (bear, #6025, 1995)
Precious™ (bear, #6104, 1998)

Prince™ (frog, #6048, 1996)
Scotch™ (bear, #6103, 1998)
Shelby™ (rabbit, #6024, 1995)
Sidney™ (rabbit, #6121, 1998)
Sire™ (lion, #6141, 1998)
Squeaky™ (mouse, #6017, 1994)

1998 BEANIE BABIES® RETIREMENTS

Baldy™ (eagle, #4074, 1997)
Bernie™ (St. Bernard, #4109, 1997)
Blackie™ (bear, #4011, 1994)
Blizzard™ (tiger, #4163, 1997)
Bones™ (dog, #4001, 1994)

Bruno™ (dog, #4183, 1997)
Crunch™ (shark, #4130, 1997)
Daisy™ (cow, #4006, 1994)
Ears™ (rabbit, #4018, 1996)
Echo™ (dolphin, #4180, 1997)

Floppity™ (bunny, #4118, 1997)
Gracie™ (swan, #4126, 1997)
Happy™ (hippo, #4061, 1994)
Hippity™ (bunny, #4119, 1997)
Hoppity™ (bunny, #4117, 1997)

1998 BEANIE BABIES®
RETIREMENTS, cont.

Inch™ (inchworm, #4044, 1995)
Inky™ (octopus, #4028, 1994)
Jolly™ (walrus, #4082, 1997)
Lucky™ (ladybug, #4040, 1994)

Patti™ (platypus, #4025, 1994)
Peanut™ (elephant, #4062, 1995)
Pinchers™ (lobster, #4026, 1994)
Puffer™ (puffin, #4181, 1997)
Quackers™ (duck, #4024, 1994)

Ringo™ (raccoon, #4014, 1996)
Rover™ (dog, #4101, 1996)
Seaweed™ (otter, #4080, 1996)
Scottie™ (Scottish terrier, #4102, 1996)
Sly™ (fox, #4115, 1996)
Snort™ (bull, #4002, 1997)

Spinner™ (spider, #4036, 1997)
Squealer™ (pig, #4005, 1994)
Stripes™ (tiger, #4065, 1995)
Twigs™ (giraffe, #4068, 1996)
Waddle™ (penguin, #4075, 1995)

Waves™ (whale, #4084, 1997)
Wrinkles™ (bulldog, #4103, 1996)
Weenie™ (dachshund, #4013, 1996)
Ziggy™ (zebra, #4063, 1995)
Zip™ (cat, #4004, 1995)

1998 TEENIE BEANIE BABIES™ RETIREMENTS

Bones™ (dog, 1998)
Bongo™ (monkey, 1998)
Doby™ (doberman, 1998)
Happy™ (hippo, 1998)

Inch™ (inchworm, 1998)
Mel™ (koala, 1998)
Peanut™ (elephant, 1998)
Pinchers™ (lobster, 1998)

Scoop™ (pelican, 1998)
Twigs™ (giraffe, 1998)
Waddle™ (penguin, 1998)
Zip™ (cat, 1998)

1998 PILLOW PALS™ RETIREMENTS

Huggy™ (bear, #3002, 1995)
Purr™ (tiger, #3016, 1997)
Snap™ (turtle, #3015, 1997)
Snuggy™ (bear, #3001, 1995)
Zulu™ (zebra, #3014, 1997)

1998 TY® PLUSH RETIREMENTS

Lovie™ (lamb, #8027, 1998)
Toffee™ (terrier, #2013, 1993)

*T*his section highlights the five most valuable *Attic Treasures* as determined by their secondary market value. Some of the pieces listed may be a variation of the piece while all values listed are for Generation 1 swing tags. See the *Variations* section on page 189 and the *Swing Tags* section on page 195 for more detailed explanations of how these issues affect secondary market value.

WOOLIE™ (#6011)
Issued 1993 — Retired 1993
Secondary Market Value: ❶-$1,300

HENRY™ (#6005)
Blue Ribbon/Gold Version
Issued 1993 — Retired 1997
Secondary Market Value: ❶-$1,200

REGGIE™ (#6004)
Navy Ribbon Version
Issued 1993 — Retired 1995
Secondary Market Value: ❶-$475

CLIFFORD™ (#6003)
Issued 1993 — Retired 1995
Secondary Market Value: ❶-$380

NICHOLAS™ (#6015)
Issued 1994 — Retired 1998
Secondary Market Value: ❶-$350

*T*his section highlights the five most valuable *Beanie Babies* as determined by their secondary market value. Some of the pieces listed are variations and are extremely rare finds.

PEANUT™ (#4062)
Dark Blue Version
Issued 1995 — Retired 1998
Secondary Market Value: ③- **$5,300**

NANA™ (#4067)
Issued 1995 — Retired 1995
Secondary Market Value: ③- **$4,300**

BROWNIE™ (#4010)
Issued 1994 — Retired 1994
Secondary Market Value: ①- **$4,200**

TEDDY™ (VIOLET) (#4055)
New Face/Employee Bear w/Red Tush Tag
Issued 1994 — Retired 1996
Secondary Market Value: No Hang Tag – **$4,000**

DERBY™ (#4008)
Fine Mane Version
Issued 1995 — Current
Secondary Market Value: ③- **$3,900**

*T*his section highlights the five most valuable *Teenie Beanie Babies* as determined by their secondary market value. Generally, the pieces from the first promotion command a higher value than those from the second, with those released earlier in the promotion having the highest values.

PINKY™
1st Promotion, #2
Issued 1997 — Retired 1997
Secondary Market Value: $55

PATTI™
1st Promotion, #1
Issued 1997 — Retired 1997
Secondary Market Value: $48

CHOPS™
1st Promotion, #3
Issued 1997 — Retired 1997
Secondary Market Value: $43

CHOCOLATE™
1st Promotion, #4
Issued 1997 — Retired 1997
Secondary Market Value: $35

SEAMORE™
1st Promotion, #7
Issued 1997 — Retired 1997
Secondary Market Value: $33

*T*his section highlights the top five most valuable *Pillow Pals* as determined by their secondary market value. As there have been relatively few *Pillow Pals* retirements thus far, there has been little secondary market activity among these pieces. Several rare variations and early retired pieces make up the top five most valuable designs.

RIBBIT™ (#3006)
Issued 1995 — Retired 1996
Secondary Market Value: $375

SNAP™ (#3007)
Issued 1995 — Retired 1996
Secondary Market Value: $365

MEOW™ (#3011)
Gray Version
Issued 1997 — Current
Secondary Market Value: $110

ZULU™ (#3014)
Thin Stripes Version
Issued 1997 — Retired 1998
Secondary Market Value: $70

ZULU™ (#3014)
Thick Stripes Version
Issued 1997 — Retired 1998
Secondary Market Value: $35

*T*his section highlights the top five most valuable *Ty Plush* pieces as determined by their secondary market value. While the line has been around since 1986, its secondary market activity is fairly new and prices for many of the older pieces have not been established. As a result, several rare and valuable pieces, such as the early Himalayan cats, do not appear on this list, but are certainly very coveted!

PAPA PUMPKIN™ (#9023)
Issued 1995 — Retired 1996
Secondary Market Value: $1,100

1991 TY COLLECTABLE BEAR™ (#5500)
Issued 1991 — Retired 1991
Secondary Market Value: $1,000

PAPA RUMPLES™ (#9022)
Issued 1995 — Retired 1996
Secondary Market Value: $980

PAPA SHAGGY™ (#9024)
Issued 1994 — Retired 1996
Secondary Market Value: $950

MAX™ (#3001)
Issued 1988 — Retired 1990
Secondary Market Value: $900

How To Use Your Collector's Value Guide™

1. Locate your piece in the Value Guide. The guide is arranged by *Attic Treasures*, *Beanie Babies*, *Teenie Beanie Babies*, *Pillow Pals* and *Ty Plush*, which is broken down by bears, cats, dogs, country and wildlife. The pieces are listed alphabetically within their collection. To find a piece more quickly, refer to the *Index By Animal Type* or *Alphabetical Index* on pages 208 and 217, respectively. Note: Some items included are prototypes and may differ slightly from the actual piece. All sizes are approximate and may vary.

2. Find the secondary market value of your piece. Some of the values are listed as "N/E," meaning the secondary market value for that particular piece has not been established. *Attic Treasures* and *Beanie Babies* secondary market

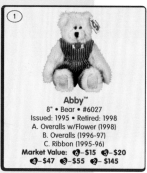

Abby™
8" • Bear • #6027
Issued: 1995 • Retired: 1998
A. Overalls w/Flower (1998)
B. Overalls (1996-97)
C. Ribbon (1995-96)
Market Value: ❻–$15 ❺–$20
❹–$47 ❸–$55 ❷–$145

values are determined by which generation tag is attached to the piece (for more details, see page 195) and the market value for each is listed next to the appropriate symbol. If a piece has a variation with a distinct secondary market value, the value is listed next to the letter or description that corresponds to the appropriate version listed above. For current pieces, fill in the current market price on the space provided (❻–$____), which is usually the price you paid. All values listed are for animals with mint condition tags.

3. Record both the original price (what you actually paid), as well as the current value of the piece. Mark the prices in the corresponding boxes at the bottom of the page. Use a pencil so you can change the totals as your collection grows!

ATTIC TREASURES™			
Date Purchased	Tag Gen.	Price Paid	Value of My Collection
1. 2/24	3	5.00	55.00
2.			
3.			
PENCIL TOTALS			

4. Calculate the total value for the entire page by adding together all of the boxes in each column. Don't forget to use pencil for this part as well.

5. Transfer the totals from each page to the *Total Value Of My Collection* worksheets. You can find this convenient chart located on pages 182-184.

6. Add all of the totals together to determine the overall value of your collection.

A WEALTH OF ATTIC TREASURES™

In 1998, there were 27 new releases and 27 retirements for the *Attic Treasures* line. Overall, there have been 92 *Attic Treasures* released since 1993 and 20 are still current. The market value for *Attic Treasures* is determined by which generation tag the piece is wearing (see *Swing Tags* section for additional information).

ATTIC TREASURES™ TAG KEY

6 – 6th Generation   **3** – 3rd Generation

5 – 5th Generation   **2** – 2nd Generation

4 – 4th Generation   **1** – 1st Generation

**① **

Abby™
8" • Bear • #6027
Issued: 1995 • Retired: 1998
A. Overalls w/Flower (1998)
B. Overalls (1996-97)
C. Ribbon (1995-96)
Market Value: 6–$15 **5**–$20
4–$47 **3**–$55 **2**– $145

② New!

Amethyst™
13" • Cat • #6131
Issued: 1998 • Retired: 1998
Market Value: 6–$22

**③ **

Barry™
8" • Bear • #6073
Issued: 1997 • Retired: 1997
Market Value: 5–$108

ATTIC TREASURES™

	Date Purchased	Tag Gen.	Price Paid	Value of My Collection
1.				
2.				
3.				
	PENCIL TOTALS			

(4) New!

Bearington™
14" • Bear • #6102
Issued: 1998 • Retired: 1998
Market Value: ⑥–$16

(5)

Benjamin™
9" • Rabbit • #6023
Issued: 1995 • Retired: 1997
A. Sweater (1996-97)
B. Ribbon (1995-96)
Market Value: ⑤–$55 ②–$122

(6) New!

Bloom™
16" • Rabbit • #6122
Issued: 1998 • Retired: 1998
Market Value: ⑥–$23

(7) New!

Bluebeary™
8" • Bear • #6080
Issued: 1998 • Current
Market Value: ⑥–$_____

ATTIC TREASURES™

	Date Purchased	Tag Gen.	Price Paid	Value of My Collection
4.				
5.				
6.				
7.				
8.				
PENCIL TOTALS				

(8) New!

Bonnie™
9" • Chick • #6075
Issued: 1998 • Current
Market Value: ⑥–$_____

Boris™
12" • Bear • #6041
Issued: 1996 • Retired: 1997
A. Vest (1996-97)
B. No Clothes (1996)
Market Value: ⑤–$45

Brewster™
9" • Dog • #6034
Issued: 1995 • Retired: 1997
A. Overalls (1996-97)
B. No Clothes (1995-96)
Market Value: ⑤–$32 ④–$42 ③–$55
②–$60 (Overalls), $70 (No Clothes)

Carlton™
16" • Bear • #6064
Issued: 1996 • Retired: 1997
A. Overalls (1996-97)
B. Ribbon (1996)
Market Value: ⑤–$40

New!

Casanova™
8" • Bear • #6073
Issued: 1998 • Current
Market Value: ⑥–$_____

Cassie™
12" • Bear • #6028
Issued: 1995 • Retired: 1997
A. Bloomers (1996-97)
B. Ribbon (1995-96)
Market Value: ⑤–$160 ④–$165 (Bloomers),
$185 (Ribbon) ③–$185 ②–$230

ATTIC TREASURES™

	Date Purchased	Tag Gen.	Price Paid	Value of My Collection
9.				
10.				
11.				
12.				
13.				
PENCIL TOTALS				

(14)

Charles™
12" • Bear • #6039
Issued: 1996 • Retired: 1997
A. Overalls (1996-97)
B. No Clothes (1996)
Market Value: ⑤–$38

(15)

Checkers™
8" • Panda • #6031
Issued: 1995 • Current
A. No Clothes (1998-Current)
B. Vest (1996-97)
C. No Clothes (1995-96)
Market Value: ⑥–$_____ ⑤–$25
④–$50 ③–$68 ②–$85

(16)

Chelsea™
8" • Bear • #6070
Issued: 1996 • Retired: 1998
Market Value: ⑥–$14 ⑤–$17

(17)

Christopher™
8" • Bear • #6071
Issued: 1996 • Retired: 1998
Market Value: ⑥–$16 ⑤–$22

Attic Treasures™

	Date Purchased	Tag Gen.	Price Paid	Value of My Collection
14.				
15.				
16.				
17.				
18.				
PENCIL TOTALS				

(18)

Clifford™
12" • Bear • #6003
Issued: 1993 • Retired: 1995
A. Green Ribbon (1994-95)
B. Red Ribbon (1993)
Market Value: ①–$380

19

Clyde™
12" • Bear • #6040
Issued: 1996 • Retired: 1997
A. Vest (1996-97)
B. No Clothes (1996)
Market Value: ⑤-$38

20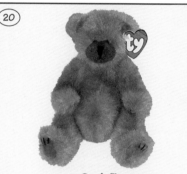

Cody™
8" • Bear • #6030
Issued: 1995 • Current
Market Value: ⑥-$_____ ⑤-$13
④-$40 ③-$50 ②-$78

21

Colby™
11" • Mouse • #6043
Issued: 1996 • Retired: 1997
A. Bloomers (1996-97)
B. No Clothes (1996)
Market Value: ⑤-$95

22

Copperfield™
16" • Bear • #6060
Issued: 1996 • Retired: 1997
A. Sweater (1996-97)
B. Ribbon (1996)
Market Value: ⑤-$56

23

Dexter™
9" • Bear • #6009
Issued: 1993 • Retired: 1997
A. Overalls (1996-97)
B. Ribbon (1993-96)
Market Value: ⑤-$22 ④-$60
③-$70 ②-$95 ①-$100

ATTIC TREASURES™

	Date Purchased	Tag Gen.	Price Paid	Value of My Collection
19.				
20.				
21.				
22.				
23.				
PENCIL TOTALS				

(24)

Dickens™
8" • Bear • #6038
Issued: 1996 • Retired: 1998
A. No Clothes (1998)
B. Overalls (1996-97)
C. No Clothes (1996)
Market Value: **6**–$16 **5**–$22 **4**–$40

(25)

Digby™
12" • Bear • #6013
Issued: 1994 • Retired: 1997
A. Vest (1996-97)
B. Ribbon (1994-96)
Market Value: **5**–$56 **4**–$80
3–N/E **2**–$90 **1**–$245

(26)

Domino™
12" • Panda • #6042
Issued: 1996 • Retired: 1997
A. Overalls (1996-97)
B. No Clothes (1996)
Market Value: **5**–$44

(27)

Ebony™
15" • Cat • #6063
Issued: 1996 • Retired: 1997
A. Bloomers (1996-97)
B. Ribbon (1996)
Market Value: **5**–$42

ATTIC TREASURES™

	Date Purchased	Tag Gen.	Price Paid	Value of My Collection
24.				
25.				
26.				
27.				
28.				
✏ PENCIL TOTALS				

(28)
New!

Ebony™
13" • Cat • #6130
Issued: 1998 • Retired: 1998
Market Value: **6**–$23

ATTIC TREASURES™

(29)

Emily™
12" • Bear • #6016
Issued: 1994 • Retired: 1997
A. Dress/Hat (1996-97)
B. Bow (1995-96)
C. Ribbon/Small Feet (1994-95)
D. Ribbon/Big Feet (1994)
Market Value: ❺–$55 ❹–$100
❸–$125 ❷–$145 ❶–$155 (Bow), $110
(Ribbon/Small Feet), $220 (Ribbon/Big Feet)

(30) New!

Eve™
12" • Bear • #6106
Issued: 1998 • Current
Market Value: ❻–$_____

(31)

Fraser™
8" • Bear • #6010
Issued: 1993 • Retired: 1998
A. Sweater (1996-98)
B. Ribbon (1993-96)
Market Value: ❻–$15
❺–$15 (Sweater), $28 (Ribbon) ❹–$53
❸–$70 ❷–$125 ❶–$300

(32)

Frederick™
8" • Bear • #6072
Issued: 1996 • Retired: 1997
Market Value: ❺–$40

(33)

Gilbert™
8" • Bear • #6006
Issued: 1993 • Retired: 1997
A. Overalls (1996-97)
B. Ribbon (1993-96)
Market Value: ❺–$25 ❶–$225

ATTIC TREASURES™

	Date Purchased	Tag Gen.	Price Paid	Value of My Collection
29.				
30.				
31.				
32.				
33.				
PENCIL TOTALS				

49

(34)

Gilbert™
8" • Bear • #6015
Issued: 1993 • Retired: 1993
Market Value: ❶–$310

(35) *New!*

Gloria™
12" • Rabbit • #6123
Issued: 1998 • Retired: 1998
Market Value: ❻–$52

(36) *New!*

Grace™
12" • Hippopotamus • #6142
Issued: 1998 • Retired: 1998
Market Value: ❻–$14

(37)

Grady™
16" • Bear • #6051
Issued: 1996 • Retired: 1997
A. Vest (1996-97)
B. Ribbon (1996)
Market Value: ❺–$64

ATTIC TREASURES™

	Date Purchased	Tag Gen.	Price Paid	Value of My Collection
34.				
35.				
36.				
37.				
38.				
✏ PENCIL TOTALS				

(38) *New!*

Grant™
13" • Bear • #6101
Issued: 1998 • Current
Market Value: ❻–$_____

(39)

Grover™
16" • Bear • #6050
Issued: 1995 • Retired: 1997
A. Overalls (1996-97)
B. Ribbon (1995-96)
Market Value: **5**–$35 **4**–$52
3–$65 **2**–$75

(40) New!

Grover™
13" • Bear • #6100
Issued: 1998 • Retired: 1998
Market Value: **6**–$23

(41)

Grover Gold™
16" • Bear • #6051
Issued: 1995 • Retired: 1997
A. Vest (Est. 1997)
B. Ribbon (Est. 1995)
Market Value: **5**–$48 **4**–$53

(42)

Heather™
20" • Rabbit • #6061
Issued: 1996 • Retired: 1997
A. Overalls (1996-97)
B. Ribbon (1996)
Market Value: **5**–$36

(43)

Henry™
8" • Bear • #6005
Issued: 1993 • Retired: 1997
A. Overalls (1996-97)
B. Green Ribbon/Brown (1994-96)
C. Blue Ribbon/Gold (1993)
D. Red Ribbon/Gold (1993)
Market Value: **5**–$30
1–$210 (Green Ribbon/Brown), $1,200
(Blue Ribbon/Gold), N/E (Red Ribbon/Gold)

ATTIC TREASURES™

	Date Purchased	Tag Gen.	Price Paid	Value of My Collection
39.				
40.				
41.				
42.				
43.				
PENCIL TOTALS				

44 New!

Iris™
10" • Rabbit • #6077
Issued: 1998 • Current
Market Value: ⑥-$_____

45

Ivan™
8" • Bear • #6029
Issued: 1995 • Current
Market Value: ⑥-$_____ ⑤-$25
④-$60 ③-$65 ②-$70

46

Ivory™
15" • Cat • #6062
Issued: 1996 • Retired: 1997
A. Overalls (1996-97)
B. Ribbon (1996)
Market Value: ⑤-$75

47 New!

Ivy™
10" • Rabbit • #6076
Issued: 1998 • Current
Market Value: ⑥-$_____

ATTIC TREASURES™

	Date Purchased	Tag Gen.	Price Paid	Value of My Collection
44.				
45.				
46.				
47.				
48.				
✏ PENCIL TOTALS				

48

Jeremy™
12" • Hare • #6008
Issued: 1993 • Retired: 1997
A. Overalls (1997)
B. Vest (1996-97)
C. Ribbon (1993-96)
Market Value: ⑤-$42 ④-$80
③-$80 ②-$115 ①-$280

49

Justin™
14" • Monkey • #6044
Issued: 1996 • Retired: 1997
A. Sweater (1996-97)
B. No Clothes (1996)
Market Value: ⑤-$53

50

King™
9" • Frog • #6049
Issued: 1996 • Retired: 1997
A. Cape (1996-97)
B. No Clothes (1996)
Market Value: ⑤-$42

51
New!

King™
11" • Frog • #6140
Issued: 1998 • Retired: 1998
Market Value: ⑥-$26

52

Lilly™
9" • Lamb • #6037
Issued: 1995 • Retired: 1998
A. Bloomers (1996-98)
B. Ribbon (1995-96)
**Market Value: ⑥-$22   ⑤-$28
④-$45   ③-$75   ②-$150**

53

Madison™
10" • Cow • #6035
Issued: 1995 • Retired: 1998
A. Overalls (1996-98)
B. Ribbon (1995-96)
**Market Value: ⑥-$18   ⑤-$23
④-$60   ③-$75   ②-$150**

ATTIC TREASURES™

	Date Purchased	Tag Gen.	Price Paid	Value of My Collection
49.				
50.				
51.				
52.				
53.				
✏ PENCIL TOTALS				

54

Malcolm™
12" • Bear • #6026
Issued: 1995 • Retired: 1997
A. Sweater (1996-97)
B. Ribbon (1995-96)
Market Value: **5**–$42 **4**–$50
3–$75 **2**–$140

55

Mason™
8" • Bear • #6020
Issued: 1995 • Retired: 1998
A. Sweater (1996-98)
B. Ribbon (1995-96)
Market Value: **6**–$18 **5**–$23
4–$50 **3**–$65 **2**–$118

56

New!

Montgomery™
15" • Moose • #6143
Issued: 1998 • Retired: 1998
Market Value: **6**–$22

57

Morgan™
8" • Monkey • #6018
Issued: 1994 • Retired: 1998
A. Vest (1996-98)
B. No Clothes/Shaved Face (1996)
C. Ribbon/Furry Face (1994-95)
Market Value: **6**–$13 **5**–$20
2–$80 **1**–$225

ATTIC TREASURES™

	Date Purchased	Tag Gen.	Price Paid	Value of My Collection
54.				
55.				
56.				
57.				
58.				
PENCIL TOTALS				

58

Murphy™
9" • Dog • #6033
Issued: 1995 • Retired: 1997
A. Overalls (1996-97)
B. No Clothes (1995-96)
Market Value: **5**–$27 **4**–$48
3–$60 **2**–$70

(59)

Nicholas™
8" • Bear • #6015
Issued: 1994 • Retired: 1998
A. Sweater (1996-98)
B. Ribbon (1994-96)
Market Value: ⑥-$20 ⑤-$23 ④-$45
③-N/E ②-N/E ①-$350

(60)

Nola™
12" • Bear • #6014
Issued: 1994 • Retired: 1997
A. Dress/Hat (1996-97)
B. Bow/Small Feet (1995-96)
C. Ribbon/Big Feet (1994-95)
Market Value: ⑤-$80 ④-$50 ③-$120
②-$140 ①-$175 (Bow/Small Feet),
$215 (Ribbon/Big Feet)

(61)

Oscar™
8" • Bear • #6025
Issued: 1995 • Retired: 1998
A. Overalls (1996-98)
B. Ribbon (1995-96)
Market Value: ⑥-$15 ⑤-$22
④-$50 ③-$50 ②-$105

(62)

Penelope™
9" • Pig • #6036
Issued: 1995 • Retired: 1997
A. Overalls (1996-97)
B. No Clothes (1995-96)
Market Value: ⑤-$58 ④-$80
③-$90 ②-$125

(63) New!

Peppermint™
8" • Polar Bear • #6074
Issued: 1998 • Current
Market Value: ⑥-$_____

ATTIC TREASURES™

	Date Purchased	Tag Gen.	Price Paid	Value of My Collection
59.				
60.				
61.				
62.				
63.				
PENCIL TOTALS				

64 New!

Piccadilly™
9" • Bear • #6069
Issued: 1998 • Current
Market Value: ⑥-$_____

65

Pouncer™
8" • Cat • #6011
Issued: 1994 • Current
A. Bloomers (1998-Current)
B. Sweater (1996-97)
C. Ribbon/Gold & White (1995-96)
D. Ribbon/Gold (1994-95)
Market Value: ⑥-$_____ ⑤-$17
④-N/E ③-$80 ②-$225 ①-N/E
(Ribbon/Gold & White), $340 (Ribbon/Gold)

66 New!

Precious™
12" • Bear • #6104
Issued: 1998 • Retired: 1998
Market Value: ⑥-$15

67

Prince™
7" • Frog • #6048
Issued: 1996 • Retired: 1998
Market Value: ⑥-$13 ⑤-$16

ATTIC TREASURES™

	Date Purchased	Tag Gen.	Price Paid	Value of My Collection
64.				
65.				
66.				
67.				
68.				
PENCIL TOTALS				

68

Priscilla™
12" • Pig • #6045
Issued: 1996 • Retired: 1997
A. Overalls (1996-97)
B. No Clothes (1996)
Market Value: ⑤-$42

(69)

Purrcy™
8" • Cat • #6022
Issued: 1995 • Current
A. Bloomers (1998-Current)
B. Overalls (1996-97)
C. Ribbon (1995-96)
**Market Value: ⑥-$_____ ⑤-$17
④-$105 ③-$105 ②-$225**

(70)

Rebecca™
12" • Bear • #6019
Issued: 1995 • Retired: 1997
A. Overalls (1996-97)
B. Bow (1995-96)
**Market Value: ⑤-$50 ④-$120
③-$130 ②-$295**

(71)

Reggie™
8" • Bear • #6004
Issued: 1993 • Retired: 1995
A. Navy Ribbon (1994-95)
B. Green Ribbon (1994)
C. Red Ribbon (1993)
**Market Value: ①-$475 (Navy Ribbon),
N/E (Green Ribbon), N/E (Red Ribbon)**

(72)
New!

Rose™
10" • Rabbit • #6078
Issued: 1998 • Current
Market Value: ⑥-$_____

(73)
New!

Samuel™
13" • Bear • #6105
Issued: 1998 • Current
Market Value: ⑥-$_____

ATTIC TREASURES™

	Date Purchased	Tag Gen.	Price Paid	Value of My Collection
69.				
70.				
71.				
72.				
73.				
✏ PENCIL TOTALS				

(74)

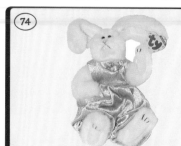

Sara™
12" • Hare • #6007
Issued: 1993 • Retired: 1997
A. Bloomers (1996-97)
B. Ribbon (1993-96)
Market Value: ❺–**$48** ❹–**$90**
❸–**$110** ❷–**$185** ❶–**$310**

(75)

New!

Sara™
15" • Rabbit • #6120
Issued: 1998 • Current
Market Value: ❻–$_____

(76)

Scooter™
9" • Dog • #6032
Issued: 1995 • Retired: 1997
A. Vest (1996-97)
B. No Clothes (1995-96)
Market Value: ❺–**$38** ❹–**$50**
❸–**$58** ❷–**$66**

(77)

New!

Scotch™
14" • Bear • #6103
Issued: 1998 • Retired: 1998
Market Value: ❻–**$23**

ATTIC TREASURES™

	Date Purchased	Tag Gen.	Price Paid	Value of My Collection
74.				
75.				
76.				
77.				
78.				
PENCIL TOTALS				

(78)

New!

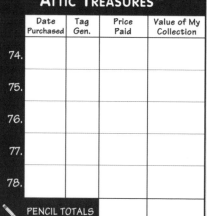

Scruffy™
9" • Dog • #6085
Issued: 1998 • Current
Market Value: ❻–$_____

(79)

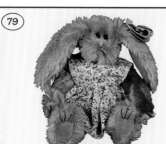

Shelby™
9" • Rabbit • #6024
Issued: 1995 • Retired: 1998
A. Dress (1996-98)
B. Ribbon (1995-96)
Market Value: ⑥–$20 ⑤–$27
④–$50 ③–$75 ②–$180

(80)
New!

Sidney™
15" • Rabbit • #6121
Issued: 1998 • Retired: 1998
Market Value: ⑥–$20

(81)
New!

Sire™
13" • Lion • #6141
Issued: 1998 • Retired: 1998
Market Value: ⑥–$20

(82)

Spencer™
15" • Dog • #6046
Issued: 1996 • Retired: 1997
A. Sweater (1996-97)
B. No Clothes (1996)
Market Value: ⑤–$45

(83)

Squeaky™
8" • Mouse • #6017
Issued: 1994 • Retired: 1998
A. No Clothes/Gray & White/Pink Nose &
White Whiskers (1995-Current)
B. Ribbon/Gray/Black Nose & Whiskers (1994)
Market Value: ⑥–$14 ⑤–$18
①–$285 (No Clothes), $210 (Ribbon)

ATTIC TREASURES™

	Date Purchased	Tag Gen.	Price Paid	Value of My Collection
79.				
80.				
81.				
82.				
83.				
PENCIL TOTALS				

84 New!

Strawbunny™
10" • Rabbit • #6079
Issued: 1998 • Current
Market Value: ⑥-$____

85

Tiny Tim™
8" • Bear • #6001
Issued: 1993 • Retired: 1997
A. Overalls (1996-97)
B. Ribbon (1993-96)
Market Value: ⑤-$24 ④-$48
③-$70 ②-$90 ①-$130

86

Tracy™
15" • Dog • #6047
Issued: 1996 • Retired: 1997
A. Overalls (1996-97)
B. No Clothes (1996)
Market Value: ⑤-$38

87

Tyler™
12" • Bear • #6002
Issued: 1993 • Retired: 1997
A. Sweater (1996-97)
B. Ribbon (1993-96)
Market Value: ⑤-$40 ④-$70
③-$75 ②-$115 ①-$170

ATTIC TREASURES™

	Date Purchased	Tag Gen.	Price Paid	Value of My Collection
84.				
85.				
86.				
87.				
88.				
✎ PENCIL TOTALS				

88

Watson™
14" • Bear • #6065
Issued: 1996 • Retired: 1997
A. Overalls (1996-97)
B. Ribbon (1996)
Market Value: ⑤-$42

(89)

Wee Willie™
8" • Bear • #6021
Issued: 1995 • Retired: 1997
A. Overalls (1996-97)
B. Ribbon (1995-96)
**Market Value: ⑤-$22 ④-$50
③-$60 ②-$70**

(90)

Whiskers™
8" • Cat • #6012
Issued: 1994 • Current
A. Bloomers (1998-Current)
B. Overalls (1996-97)
C. Ribbon/Gray & White (1995-96)
D. Ribbon/Gray (1994-95)
Market Value: ⑥-$_____ ⑤-$20 ①-$330

(91)

Woolie™
6" • Bear • #6011
Issued: 1993 • Retired: 1993
Market Value: ①-$1,300

(92)

Woolie™
6" • Bear • #6012
(appears in 1993 Ty® catalog,
production not confirmed)
Issued: 1993 • Retired: 1993
Market Value: N/E

Attic Treasures™

	Date Purchased	Tag Gen.	Price Paid	Value of My Collection
89.				
90.				
91.				
92.				
PENCIL TOTALS				

BEANIE BABIES® – A STAR IS BORN

Since it began to take the world by storm with its debut in 1994, the *Beanie Babies* family has grown to 154 pieces, while only 56 are still current. In 1998, 27 new releases have been announced and a whopping 40 *Beanie Babies* have retired.

The market value for *Beanie Babies* is determined by which generation tag the piece is wearing (see chart below and the *Swing Tags* section beginning on page 195 for additional information).

Recently, some *Beanie Babies* have been featured in promotions for various professional sports leagues. These pieces are noted in the Value Guide with a sports-related symbol in the upper right corner of their box.

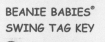

**BEANIE BABIES®
SWING TAG KEY**

 ⑤ – 5th Generation

 ④ – 4th Generation

 ③ – 3rd Generation

 ② – 2nd Generation

 ① – 1st Generation

A complete listing of these promotions is included in the *Sports Promotion Beanie Babies®* section on pages 94-95 (see chart below for explanation of symbols).

SPORTS PROMOTION BEANIE BABIES® KEY

Canadian Special Olympics

 National Football League

Major League Baseball

 National Hockey League

 National Basketball Association

 Women's National Basketball Association

BEANIE BABIES®

	Date Purchased	Tag Gen.	Price Paid	Value of My Collection
1.				
PENCIL TOTALS				

1997 Teddy™
10" • Bear • #4200 • Born: 12/25/96
Issued: 10/97 • Retired: 12/97
Market Value: ④ –$65

2

Ally™
12" • Alligator • #4032 • Born: 3/14/94
Issued: 6/94 • Retired: 10/97
Market Value: ④–**$65** ③–**$135**
②–**$230** ①–**$350**

3
New!

Ants™
12" • Anteater • #4195 • Born: 11/7/97
Issued: 5/98 • Current
Market Value: ⑤–**$_____**

4

Baldy™
8" • Eagle • #4074 • Born: 2/17/96
Issued: 5/97 • Retired: 5/98
Market Value: ⑤–**$22** ④–**$30**

5

Batty™
5" • Bat • #4035 • Born: 10/29/96
Issued: 10/97 • Current
Market Value: ⑤–**$_____** ④–**$25**

6

Bernie™
10" • St. Bernard • #4109 • Born: 10/3/96
Issued: 1/97 • Retired: 9/98
Market Value: ⑤–**$12** ④–**$16**

BEANIE BABIES®

	Date Purchased	Tag Gen.	Price Paid	Value of My Collection
2.				
3.				
4.				
5.				
6.				
PENCIL TOTALS				

7

Bessie™
10" • Cow • #4009 • Born: 6/27/95
Issued: 6/95 • Retired: 10/97
Market Value: ④–$75 ③–$155

8

Blackie™
10" • Bear • #4011 • Born: 7/15/94
Issued: 6/94 • Retired: 9/98
Market Value: ⑤–$12 ④–$18
③–$110 ②–$215 ①–$330

9

Blizzard™
10" • Tiger • #4163 • Born: 12/12/96
Issued: 5/97 • Retired: 5/98
Market Value: ⑤–$28 ④–$40

10

Bones™
10" • Dog • #4001 • Born: 1/18/94
Issued: 6/94 • Retired: 5/98
Market Value: ⑤–$22 ④–$28
③–$125 ②–$230 ①–$335

Beanie Babies®

	Date Purchased	Tag Gen.	Price Paid	Value of My Collection
7.				
8.				
9.				
10.				
11.				
PENCIL TOTALS				

11

A

B

Bongo™
(name changed from "Nana™" in 1995)
9" • Monkey • #4067 • Born: 8/17/95
Issued: 6/95 • Current
Market Value:
A. Tan Tail (6/95-Current)
⑤–$_____ ④–$17 ③–$150
B. Brown Tail (2/96-6/96) ④–$80 ③–$160

⑫ New!

Britannia™
(exclusive to Great Britain)
10" • Bear • #4601 • Born: 12/15/97
Issued: 12/97 • Current
Market Value: ⑤–$550 (in U.S. market)

⑬

Bronty™
7" • Brontosaurus • #4085 • Born: N/A
Issued: 6/95 • Retired: 6/96
Market Value: ③–$1,100

⑭

Brownie™
(name changed to "Cubbie™" in 1994)
10" • Bear • #4010 • Born: N/A
Issued: 1/94 • Retired: 1994
Market Value: ①–$4,200

⑮ New!

Bruno™
10" • Dog • #4183 • Born: 9/9/97
Issued: 12/97 • Retired: 9/98
Market Value: ⑤–$12

⑯

Bubbles™
8" • Fish • #4078 • Born: 7/2/95
Issued: 6/95 • Retired: 5/97
Market Value: ④–$185   ③–$260

BEANIE BABIES®

	Date Purchased	Tag Gen.	Price Paid	Value of My Collection
12.				
13.				
14.				
15.				
16.				
✏ PENCIL TOTALS				

BEANIE BABIES®

17

Bucky™
11" • Beaver • #4016 • Born: 6/8/95
Issued: 1/96 • Retired: 12/97
Market Value: ④–**$45** ③–**$120**

18

Bumble™
6" • Bee • #4045 • Born: 10/16/95
Issued: 6/95 • Retired: 6/96
Market Value: ④–**$730** ③–**$650**

19

Caw™
10" • Crow • #4071 • Born: N/A
Issued: 6/95 • Retired: 6/96
Market Value: ③–**$735**

20

Chilly™
10" • Polar Bear • #4012 • Born: N/A
Issued: 6/94 • Retired: 1/96
Market Value: ③–**$2,200**
②–**$2,300** ①–**$2,500**

BEANIE BABIES®

	Date Purchased	Tag Gen.	Price Paid	Value of My Collection
17.				
18.				
19.				
20.				
21.				
✏ PENCIL TOTALS				

21

Chip™
10" • Cat • #4121 • Born: 1/26/96
Issued: 5/97 • Current
Market Value: ⑤–$_____ ④–**$18**

(22)

Chocolate™
10" • Moose • #4015 • Born: 4/27/93
Issued: 1/94 • Current
Market Value: ⑤–$_____ ④–$16
③–$115 ②–$225 ①–$330

(23)

Chops™
8" • Lamb • #4019 • Born: 5/3/96
Issued: 1/96 • Retired: 1/97
Market Value: ④–$195 ③–$280

(24)

✓

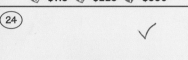

Claude™
10" • Crab • #4083 • Born: 9/3/96
Issued: 5/97 • Current
Market Value: ⑤–$_____ ④–$18

(25)

New!

Clubby™
(exclusive to Beanie Babies®
Official Club members)
10" • Bear • N/A • Born: 7/7/98
Issued: 5/98 • Current
Market Value: ⑤–$_____

(26)

Congo™
8" • Gorilla • #4160 • Born: 11/9/96
Issued: 6/96 • Current
Market Value: ⑤–$_____ ④–$14

BEANIE BABIES®

	Date Purchased	Tag Gen.	Price Paid	Value of My Collection
22.				
23.				
24.				
25.				
26.				
PENCIL TOTALS				

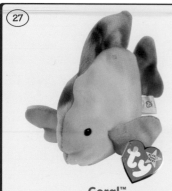

Coral™
8" • Fish • #4079 • Born: 3/2/95
Issued: 6/95 • Retired: 1/97
Market Value: ④–**$205** ③–**$300**

Crunch™
8" • Shark • #4130 • Born: 1/13/96
Issued: 1/97 • Retired: 9/98
Market Value: ⑤–**$12** ④–**$14**

Cubbie™
(name changed from "Brownie™" in 1994)
10" • Bear • #4010 • Born: 11/14/93
Issued: 1/94 • Retired: 12/97
Market Value: ⑤–**$35** ④–**$35**
③–**$130** ②–**$245** ①–**$360**

Curly™
10" • Bear • #4052 • Born: 4/12/96
Issued: 6/96 • Current
Market Value: ⑤–$_____ ④–**$30**

BEANIE BABIES®

	Date Purchased	Tag Gen.	Price Paid	Value of My Collection
27.				
28.				
29.				
30.				
31.				
✏ PENCIL TOTALS				

Daisy™
10" • Cow • #4006 • Born: 5/10/94
Issued: 6/94 • Retired: 9/98
Market Value: ⑤–**$12** ④–**$16**
③–**$110** ②–**$245** ①–**$340**

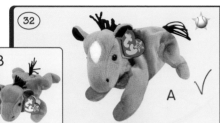

32

Derby™
10" • Horse • #4008 • Born: 9/16/95
Issued: 6/95 • Current
Market Value:
A. Star (12/97-Current) ⑤–$____
B. Coarse Mane (Est. Late 95-12/97)
④–**$40** ③–**$750**
C. Fine Mane (Est. 6/95-Late 95)
③–**$3,900**

B

C

33

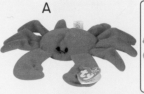

Digger™
10" • Crab • #4027 • Born: 8/23/95
Issued: 6/94 • Retired: 5/97
Market Value:
A. Red (6/95-5/97) ④–**$145** ③–**$330**
B. Orange (6/94-6/95) ③–**$825**
②–**$900** ①–**$950**

34

Doby™
10" • Doberman • #4110 • Born: 10/9/96
Issued: 1/97 • Current
Market Value: ⑤–$____ ④–**$13**

35

Doodle™
(name changed to "Strut™" in 1997)
8" • Rooster • #4171 • Born: 3/8/96
Issued: 5/97 • Retired: 1997
Market Value: ④–**$55**

36

Dotty™
10" • Dalmatian • #4100 • Born: 10/17/96
Issued: 5/97 • Current
Market Value: ⑤–$____ ④–**$15**

BEANIE BABIES®

	Date Purchased	Tag Gen.	Price Paid	Value of My Collection
32.				
33.				
34.				
35.				
36.				
✏ PENCIL TOTALS				

BEANIE BABIES®

69

37

New!

Early™
8" • Robin • #4190 • Born: 2/20/97 or 3/20/97
Issued: 5/98 • Current
Market Value: ⑤–$_____

38

Ears™
9" • Rabbit • #4018 • Born: 4/18/95
Issued: 1/96 • Retired: 5/98
Market Value: ⑤–$20 ④–$28 ③–$110

39

Echo™
10" • Dolphin • #4180 • Born: 12/21/96
Issued: 5/97 • Retired: 5/98
Market Value: ⑤–$20 ④–$28

40

New!

Erin™
10" • Bear • #4186 • Born: 3/17/97
Issued: 1/98 • Current
Market Value: ⑤–$_____

BEANIE BABIES®

	Date Purchased	Tag Gen.	Price Paid	Value of My Collection
37.				
38.				
39.				
40.				
41.				
✏ PENCIL TOTALS				

41

New!

Fetch™
9" • Golden Retriever • #4189 • Born: 2/4/97
Issued: 5/98 • Current
Market Value: ⑤–$_____

(42)

Flash™
10" • Dolphin • #4021 • Born: 5/13/93
Issued: 1/94 • Retired: 5/97
Market Value: **④–$145** **③–$230**
②–$350 **①–$450**

(43)

Fleece™
9" • Lamb • #4125 • Born: 3/21/96
Issued: 1/97 • Current
Market Value: **⑤–$_____** **④–$13**

(44)

Flip™
10" • Cat • #4012 • Born: 2/28/95
Issued: 1/96 • Retired: 10/97
Market Value: **④–$45** **③–$160**

(45)

Floppity™
10" • Bunny • #4118 • Born: 5/28/96
Issued: 1/97 • Retired: 5/98
Market Value: **⑤–$23** **④–$30**

(46)

Flutter™
6" • Butterfly • #4043 • Born: N/A
Issued: 6/95 • Retired: 6/96
Market Value: **③–$1,150**

BEANIE BABIES®

	Date Purchased	Tag Gen.	Price Paid	Value of My Collection
42.				
43.				
44.				
45.				
46.				
✏ PENCIL TOTALS				

Fortune™
10" • Panda • #4196 • Born: 12/6/97
Issued: 5/98 • Current
Market Value: ⑤–$_____

Freckles™
10" • Leopard • #4066 • Born: 6/3/96 or 7/28/96
Issued: 6/96 • Current
Market Value: ⑤–$_____ ④–$13

Garcia™
10" • Bear • #4051 • Born: 8/1/95
Issued: 1/96 • Retired: 5/97
Market Value: ④–$195 ③–$275

Gigi™
8" • Poodle • #4191 • Born: 4/7/97
Issued: 5/98 • Current
Market Value: ⑤–$_____

BEANIE BABIES®

	Date Purchased	Tag Gen.	Price Paid	Value of My Collection
47.				
48.				
49.				
50.				
51.				
✏ PENCIL TOTALS				

Glory™
10" • Bear • #4188 • Born: 7/4/97
Issued: 5/98 • Current
Market Value: ⑤–$_____

52

Gobbles™
8" • Turkey • #4034 • Born: 11/27/96
Issued: 10/97 • Current
Market Value: ⑤-$_____ ④-$30

53

Goldie™
8" • Goldfish • #4023 • Born: 11/14/94
Issued: 6/94 • Retired: 12/97
Market Value: ⑤-$50 ④-$50
③-$135 ②-$250 ①-$375

54

Gracie™
8" • Swan • #4126 • Born: 6/17/96
Issued: 1/97 • Retired: 5/98
Market Value: ⑤-$20 ④-$28

55

Grunt™
10" • Razorback • #4092 • Born: 7/19/95
Issued: 1/96 • Retired: 5/97
Market Value: ④-$190 ③-$300

56

B

A

Happy™
10" • Hippo • #4061 • Born: 2/25/94
Issued: 6/94 • Retired: 5/98
Market Value:
A. Lavender (6/95-5/98)
⑤-$25 ④-$32 ③-$310
B. Gray (6/94-6/95)
③-$780 ②-$825 ①-$900

BEANIE BABIES®

	Date Purchased	Tag Gen.	Price Paid	Value of My Collection
52.				
53.				
54.				
55.				
56.				
PENCIL TOTALS				

(57)

Hippity™
10" • Bunny • #4119 • Born: 6/1/96
Issued: 1/97 • Retired: 5/98
Market Value: ⑤–$23 ④–$30

(58) New!

Hissy™
25" • Snake • #4185 • Born: 4/4/97
Issued: 12/97 • Current
Market Value: ⑤–$____

(59)

Hoot™
6" • Owl • #4073 • Born: 8/9/95
Issued: 1/96 • Retired: 10/97
Market Value: ④–$50 ③–$130

(60)

Hoppity™
10" • Bunny • #4117 • Born: 4/3/96
Issued: 1/97 • Retired: 5/98
Market Value: ⑤–$23 ④–$30

Beanie Babies®

	Date Purchased	Tag Gen.	Price Paid	Value of My Collection
57.				
58.				
59.				
60.				
61.				
PENCIL TOTALS				

(61)

Humphrey™
10" • Camel • #4060 • Born: N/A
Issued: 6/94 • Retired: 6/95
Market Value: ③–$2,000
②–$2,100 ①–$2,200

62 New!

Iggy™
(commonly mistagged as "Rainbow™")
10" • Iguana • #4038 • Born: 8/12/97
Issued: 12/97 • Current
Market Value: ⑤-$_____

63

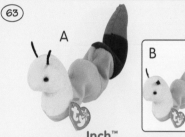

A

B

Inch™
12" • Inchworm • #4044 • Born: 9/3/95
Issued: 6/95 • Retired: 5/98
Market Value:
A. Yarn Antennas (Est. Mid 96-5/98)
⑤-$23 ④-$33
B. Felt Antennas (Est. 6/95-Mid 96)
④-$190 ③-$215

64

A

B

C

Inky™
8" • Octopus • #4028 • Born: 11/29/94
Issued: 6/94 • Retired: 5/98
Market Value:
A. Pink (6/95-5/98)
⑤-$38 ④-$45 ③-$330
B. Tan With Mouth (9/94-6/95)
③-$750 ②-$775
C. Tan Without Mouth (6/94-9/94)
②-$800 ①-$825

65 New!

Jabber™
10" • Parrot • #4197 • Born: 10/10/97
Issued: 5/98 • Current
Market Value: ⑤-$_____

66 New!

Jake™
9" • Mallard Duck • #4199 • Born: 4/16/97
Issued: 5/98 • Current
Market Value: ⑤-$_____

BEANIE BABIES®

	Date Purchased	Tag Gen.	Price Paid	Value of My Collection
62.				
63.				
64.				
65.				
66.				
PENCIL TOTALS				

BEANIE BABIES®

67

Jolly™
10" • Walrus • #4082 • Born: 12/2/96
Issued: 5/97 • Retired: 5/98
Market Value: ⑤–$25 ④–$32

68

Kiwi™
10" • Toucan • #4070 • Born: 9/16/95
Issued: 6/95 • Retired: 1/97
Market Value: ④–$205 ③–$310

69 New!

Kuku™
10" • Cockatoo • #4192 • Born: 1/5/97
Issued: 5/98 • Current
Market Value: ⑤–$_____

70

Lefty™
8" • Donkey • #4085 • Born: 7/4/96
Issued: 6/96 • Retired: 1/97
Market Value: ④–$360

BEANIE BABIES®

	Date Purchased	Tag Gen.	Price Paid	Value of My Collection
67.				
68.				
69.				
70.				
71.				
✎ PENCIL TOTALS				

71

Legs™
10" • Frog • #4020 • Born: 4/25/93
Issued: 1/94 • Retired: 10/97
Market Value: ④–$32 ③–$115
②–$245 ①–$335

(72)

Libearty™
10" • Bear • #4057 • Born: Summer 1996
Issued: 6/96 • Retired: 1/97
Market Value: ④–**$420**

(73)

A

B

Lizzy™
12" • Lizard • #4033 • Born: 5/11/95
Issued: 6/95 • Retired: 12/97
Market Value:
A. Blue (1/96-12/97)
⑤–**$32** ④–**$32** ③–**$360**
B. Tie-dye (6/95-1/96) ③–**$1,060**

(74)

A

B

C

Lucky™
6" • Ladybug • #4040 • Born: 5/1/95
Issued: 6/94 • Retired: 5/98
Market Value:
A. Approx. 11 Printed Spots
(2/96-5/98) ⑤–**$26** ④–**$35**
B. Approx. 21 Printed Spots
(Est. Mid 96-Late 96) ④–**$625**
C. Approx. 7 Felt Glued-On Spots
(6/94-2/96) ③–**$215**
②–**$310** ①–**$400**

(75)

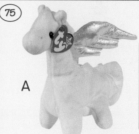

A

B

Magic™
10" • Dragon • #4088 • Born: 9/5/95
Issued: 6/95 • Retired: 12/97
Market Value:
A. Pale Pink Thread (6/95-12/97)
④–**$52** ③–**$120**
B. Hot Pink Thread (Est. Mid 96-Early 97) ④–**$80**

(76)

Manny™
9" • Manatee • #4081 • Born: 6/8/95
Issued: 1/96 • Retired: 5/97
Market Value: ④–**$180** ③–**$250**

BEANIE BABIES®

	Date Purchased	Tag Gen.	Price Paid	Value of My Collection
72.				
73.				
74.				
75.				
76.				
PENCIL TOTALS				

77

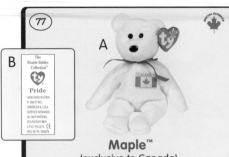

B

The
Beanie Babies
Collection™

Pride

HANDMADE IN CHINA
© 1997 TY INC.
OAKBROOK IL, USA
SURFACE WASHABLE
ALL NEW MATERIAL
POLYESTER FIBER
& PVC PELLETS CE
REG. NO PA 1965(KY)

Maple™
(exclusive to Canada)
10" • Bear • #4600 • Born: 7/1/96
Issued: 1/97 • Current
Market Value:
A. "Maple™" Tush Tag (Est. Early 97-Current)
⑤–**$295 (in U.S. market)** ④–**$295**
B. "Pride™" Tush Tag (Est. Early 97) ④–**$670**

78

Mel™
8" • Koala • #4162 • Born: 1/15/96
Issued: 1/97 • Current
Market Value: ⑤–$_____ ④–**$13**

79

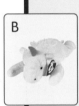

B

C

Mystic™
10" • Unicorn • #4007 • Born: 5/21/94
Issued: 6/94 • Current
Market Value:
A. Iridescent Horn (10/97-Current)
⑤–$_____ ④–**$35**
B. Brown Horn/Coarse Mane (Est.
Late 95-10/97) ④–**$45** ③–**$110**
C. Brown Horn/Fine Mane
(Est. 6/94-Late 95) ③–**$285**
②–**$375** ①–**$490**

80

Nana™
(name changed to "Bongo™" in 1995)
9" • Monkey • #4067 • Born: N/A
Issued: 6/95 • Retired: 1995
Market Value: ③–**$4,300**

BEANIE BABIES®

	Date Purchased	Tag Gen.	Price Paid	Value of My Collection
77.				
78.				
79.				
80.				
81.				
PENCIL TOTALS				

81

Nanook™
10" • Husky • #4104 • Born: 11/21/96
Issued: 5/97 • Current
Market Value: ⑤–$_____ ④–**$16**

82

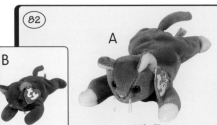

B

C

Nip™
10" • Cat • #4003 • Born: 3/6/94
Issued: 1/95 • Retired: 12/97
Market Value:
A. White Paws (3/96-12/97)
⑤-$34 **④-$34** **③-$330**
B. All Gold (1/96-3/96) **③-$950**
C. White Face (1/95-1/96)
③-$525 **②-$560**

83

Nuts™
8" • Squirrel • #4114 • Born: 1/21/96
Issued: 1/97 • Current
Market Value: **⑤-$_____** **④-$13**

84

B

A

Patti™
10" • Platypus • #4025 • Born: 1/6/93
Issued: 1/94 • Retired: 5/98
Market Value:
A. Magenta (2/95-5/98) **⑤-$28**
④-$35 **③-$280**
B. Maroon (1/94-2/95) **③-$900**
②-$1,150 **①-$1,250**

85

Peace™
10" • Bear • #4053 • Born: 2/1/96
Issued: 5/97 • Current
Market Value: **⑤-$_____** **④-$38**

86

B

A

Peanut™
10" • Elephant • #4062 • Born: 1/25/95
Issued: 6/95 • Retired: 5/98
Market Value:
A. Light Blue (10/95-5/98) **⑤-$25**
④-$31 **③-$1,300**
B. Dark Blue (6/95-10/95) **③-$5,300**

BEANIE BABIES®

	Date Purchased	Tag Gen.	Price Paid	Value of My Collection
82.				
83.				
84.				
85.				
86.				
PENCIL TOTALS				

(87)

Peking™
10" • Panda • #4013 • Born: N/A
Issued: 6/94 • Retired: 1/96
Market Value: ③-**$2,200**
②-**$2,350** ①-**$2,400**

(88)

A

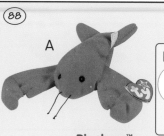

B

The Beanie Babies Collection
Punchers™ style 4026
© 1993 Ty Inc. Oakbrook, IL USA
All Rights Reserved. Caution:
Remove this tag before giving
toy to a child. For ages 3 and up.
Handmade in Korea.
Surface
Wash.

Pinchers™
10" • Lobster • #4026 • Born: 6/19/93
Issued: 1/94 • Retired: 5/98
Market Value:
A. "Pinchers™" Swing Tag (1/94-5/98) ⑤-**$26**
④-**$32** ③-**$110** ②-**$215** ①-**$320**
B. "Punchers™" Swing Tag (Est. Early 94)
①-**$3,700**

(89)

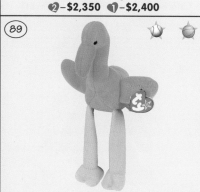

Pinky™
10" • Flamingo • #4072 • Born: 2/13/95
Issued: 6/95 • Current
Market Value: ⑤-$_____ ④-**$15** ③-**$115**

(90)

Pouch™
8" • Kangaroo • #4161 • Born: 11/6/96
Issued: 1/97 • Current
Market Value: ⑤-$_____ ④-**$16**

BEANIE BABIES®

	Date Purchased	Tag Gen.	Price Paid	Value of My Collection
87.				
88.				
89.				
90.				
91.				
✏ PENCIL TOTALS				

(91)

New!

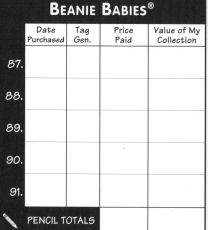

Pounce™
10" • Cat • #4122 • Born: 8/28/97
Issued: 12/97 • Current
Market Value: ⑤-$_____

(92) New!

Prance™
10" • Cat • #4123 • Born: 11/20/97
Issued: 12/97 • Current
Market Value: ⑤-$_____

(93)

A

B

The
Beanie Babies
Collection®

Princess™

HANDMADE IN CHINA
© 1997 TY INC.
OAKBROOK, IL U.S.A
SURFACE WASHABLE
ALL NEW MATERIAL
POLYESTER FIBER
& P.V.C. PELLETS
REG NO. PA. 1965(KR)

Princess™
10" • Bear • #4300 • Born: N/A
Issued: 10/97 • Current
Market Value:
A. "P.E. Pellets" On Tush Tag
(Est. Late 97-Current) ④-$_____
B. "P.V.C. Pellets" On Tush Tag
(Est. Late 97) ④-**$130**

(94) New!

Puffer™
9" • Puffin • #4181 • Born: 11/3/97
Issued: 12/97 • Retired: 9/98
Market Value: ⑤-**$12**

(95)

Pugsly™
10" • Pug Dog • #4106 • Born: 5/2/96
Issued: 5/97 • Current
Market Value: ⑤-$_____ ④-**$18**

BEANIE BABIES®

	Date Purchased	Tag Gen.	Price Paid	Value of My Collection
92.				
93.				
94.				
95.				
✏ PENCIL TOTALS				

BEANIE BABIES®

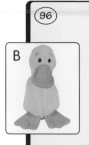

96
B / A

97

Quackers™
8" • Duck • #4024 • Born: 4/19/94
Issued: 6/94 • Retired: 5/98
Market Value:
A. "Quackers™" With Wings (1/95-5/98)
⑤–$23 ④–$29 ③–$110 ②–$550
B. "Quacker™" Without Wings (6/94-1/95)
②–$2,300 ①–$2,400

Radar™
6" • Bat • #4091 • Born: 10/30/95
Issued: 9/95 • Retired: 5/97
Market Value: ④–$180 ③–$265

98
New!

B / A

99

Rainbow™
(commonly mistagged as "Iggy™")
10" • Chameleon • #4037 • Born: 10/14/97
Issued: 12/97 • Current
Market Value:
A. Tongue (6/98-Current) ⑤–$_____
B. No Tongue (12/97-6/98) ⑤–$17

Rex™
7" • Tyrannosaurus • #4086 • Born: N/A
Issued: 6/95 • Retired: 6/96
Market Value: ③–$950

BEANIE BABIES®

	Date Purchased	Tag Gen.	Price Paid	Value of My Collection
96.				
97.				
98.				
99.				
100.				
✏ PENCIL TOTALS				

100

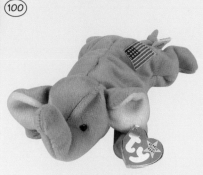

Righty™
10" • Elephant • #4086 • Born: 7/4/96
Issued: 6/96 • Retired: 1/97
Market Value: ④–$360

Ringo™
12" • Raccoon • #4014 • Born: 7/14/95
Issued: 1/96 • Retired: 9/98
Market Value: ⑤–**$12** ④–**$17** ③–**$105**

Roary™
10" • Lion • #4069 • Born: 2/20/96
Issued: 5/97 • Current
Market Value: ⑤–$_____ ④–**$15**

New!

Rocket™
9" • Blue Jay • #4202 • Born: 3/12/97
Issued: 5/98 • Current
Market Value: ⑤–$_____

Rover™
8" • Dog • #4101 • Born: 5/30/96
Issued: 6/96 • Retired: 5/98
Market Value: ⑤–**$25** ④–**$32**

Scoop™
8" • Pelican • #4107 • Born: 7/1/96
Issued: 6/96 • Current
Market Value: ⑤–$_____ ④–**$15**

BEANIE BABIES®

	Date Purchased	Tag Gen.	Price Paid	Value of My Collection
101.				
102.				
103.				
104.				
105.				
✏ PENCIL TOTALS				

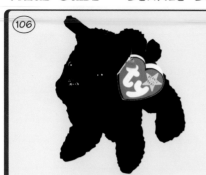

Scottie™
8" • Scottish Terrier • #4102
Born: 6/3/96 or 6/15/96
Issued: 6/96 • Retired: 5/98
Market Value: ⑤–$30 ④–$38

Seamore™
8" • Seal • #4029 • Born: 12/14/96
Issued: 6/94 • Retired: 10/97
**Market Value: ④–$180 ③–$270
②–$365 ①–$490**

Seaweed™
8" • Otter • #4080 • Born: 3/19/96
Issued: 1/96 • Retired: 9/98
Market Value: ⑤–$20 ④–$28 ③–$130

Slither™
23" • Snake • #4031 • Born: N/A
Issued: 6/94 • Retired: 6/95
**Market Value: ③–$2,150
②–$2,250 ①–$2,350**

BEANIE BABIES®

	Date Purchased	Tag Gen.	Price Paid	Value of My Collection
106.				
107.				
108.				
109.				
110.				
PENCIL TOTALS				

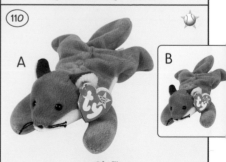

A   B

Sly™
10" • Fox • #4115 • Born: 9/12/96
Issued: 6/96 • Retired: 9/98
Market Value:
A. White Belly (8/96-9/98) ⑤–$12 ④–$18
B. Brown Belly (6/96-8/96) ④–$175

(111) New!

Smoochy™
10" • Frog • #4039 • Born: 10/1/97
Issued: 12/97 • Current
Market Value: ⑤-$_____

(112)

Snip™
10" • Siamese Cat • #4120 • Born: 10/22/96
Issued: 1/97 • Current
Market Value: ⑤-$_____ ④-$15

(113)

Snort™
10" • Bull • #4002 • Born: 5/15/95
Issued: 1/97 • Retired: 9/98
Market Value: ⑤-$12 ④-$16

(114)

Snowball™
8" • Snowman • #4201 • Born: 12/22/96
Issued: 10/97 • Retired: 12/97
Market Value: ④-$55

(115)

Sparky™
10" • Dalmatian • #4100 • Born: 2/27/96
Issued: 6/96 • Retired: 5/97
Market Value: ④-$140

BEANIE BABIES®

	Date Purchased	Tag Gen.	Price Paid	Value of My Collection
111.				
112.				
113.				
114.				
115.				
✏ PENCIL TOTALS				

116

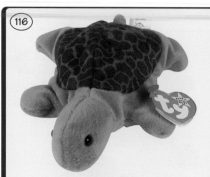

Speedy™
7" • Turtle • #4030 • Born: 8/14/94
Issued: 6/94 • Retired: 10/97
Market Value: ④–**$42** ③–**$130**
②–**$255** ①–**$350**

117

Spike™
10" • Rhinoceros • #4060 • Born: 8/13/96
Issued: 6/96 • Current
Market Value: ⑤–$_____ ④–**$15**

118

A

B

Spinner™
8" • Spider • #4036 • Born: 10/28/96
Issued: 10/97 • Retired: 9/98
Market Value:
A. "Spinner™" Tush Tag (10/97-9/98)
⑤–**$12** ④–**$22**
B. "Creepy™" Tush Tag (Est. Late 97-9/98)
⑤–**N/E**

119

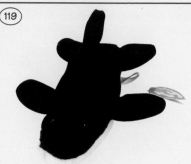

Splash™
10" • Whale • #4022 • Born: 7/8/93
Issued: 1/94 • Retired: 5/97
Market Value: ④–**$150** ③–**$240**
②–**$375** ①–**$475**

Beanie Babies®

	Date Purchased	Tag Gen.	Price Paid	Value of My Collection
116.				
117.				
118.				
119.				
120.				
✏ PENCIL TOTALS				

120

A

B

Spooky™
8" • Ghost • #4090 • Born: 10/31/95
Issued: 9/95 • Retired: 12/97
Market Value:
A. "Spooky™" Swing Tag (Est. Late 95-12/97)
④–**$42** ③–**$130**
B. "Spook™" Swing Tag (Est. 9/95-Late 95)
③–**$360**

(121)

A

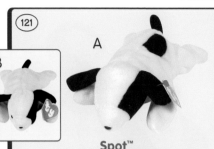

B

Spot™
10" • Dog • #4000 • Born: 1/3/93
Issued: 1/94 • Retired: 10/97
Market Value:
A. With Spot (4/94-10/97) ④–**$60**
③–**$135** ②–**$865**
B. Without Spot (1/94-4/94)
②–**$2,100** ①–**$2,200**

(122)

New!

Spunky™
10" • Cocker Spaniel • #4184 • Born: 1/14/97
Issued: 12/97 • Current
Market Value: ⑤–$_____

(123)

Squealer™
10" • Pig • #4005 • Born: 4/23/93
Issued: 1/94 • Retired: 5/98
Market Value: ⑤–**$33** ④–**$40**
③–**$130** ②–**$250** ①–**$335**

(124)

Steg™
9" • Stegosaurus • #4087 • Born: N/A
Issued: 6/95 • Retired: 6/96
Market Value: ③–**$1,025**

(125)

Sting™
10" • Stingray • #4077 • Born: 8/27/95
Issued: 6/95 • Retired: 1/97
Market Value: ④–**$225** ③–**$300**

BEANIE BABIES®

	Date Purchased	Tag Gen.	Price Paid	Value of My Collection
121.				
122.				
123.				
124.				
125.				
PENCIL TOTALS				

126 New!

Stinger™
12" • Scorpion • #4193 • Born: 9/29/97
Issued: 5/98 • Current
Market Value: ⑤–$_____

127

Stinky™
10" • Skunk • #4017 • Born: 2/13/95
Issued: 6/95 • Current
Market Value: ⑤–$_____ ④–$15 ③–$105

128 New!

Stretch™
12" • Ostrich • #4182 • Born: 9/21/97
Issued: 12/97 • Current
Market Value: ⑤–$_____

129

A

Stripes™
10" • Tiger • #4065 • Born: 6/11/95
Issued: Est. 6/95 • Retired: 5/98
Market Value:
A. Light w/Fewer Stripes
(6/96-5/98) ⑤–$20 ④–$26
B. Dark w/Fuzzy Belly
(Est. Early 96-6/96) ③–$900
C. Dark w/More Stripes
(Est. 6/95-Early 96) ③–$360

B

C

BEANIE BABIES®

	Date Purchased	Tag Gen.	Price Paid	Value of My Collection
126.				
127.				
128.				
129.				
130.				
PENCIL TOTALS				

130

Strut™
(name changed from "Doodle™" in 1997)
8" • Rooster • #4171 • Born: 3/8/96
Issued: 7/97 • Current
Market Value: ⑤–$_____ ④–$25

(131)

Tabasco™
10" • Bull • #4002 • Born: 5/15/95
Issued: 6/95 • Retired: 1/97
Market Value: ④–**$215** ③–**$280**

(132)

Tank™
9" • Armadillo • #4031
Born: 2/22/95
Issued: Est. 1/96 • Retired: 10/97
Market Value:
A. 9 Plates/With Shell
(Est. Late 96-10/97) ④–**$78**
B. 9 Plates/Without Shell
(Est. Mid 96-Late 96) ④–**$210**
C. 7 Plates/Without Shell
(Est. 1/96-Mid 96) ③–**$200**

(133)

Teddy™ (brown)
10" • Bear • #4050 • Born: 11/28/95
Issued: 6/94 • Retired: 10/97
Market Value:
A. New Face (1/95-10/97) ④–**$95**
③–**$345** ②–**$850**
B. Old Face (6/94-1/95) ②–**$2,900** ①–**$3,100**

(134)

Teddy™ (cranberry)
10" • Bear • #4052 • Born: N/A
Issued: 6/94 • Retired: 1/96
Market Value:
A. New Face (1/95-1/96) ③–**$2,000** ②–**$2,100**
B. Old Face (6/94-1/95) ②–**$2,000** ①–**$2,100**

(135)

Teddy™ (jade)
10" • Bear • #4057 • Born: N/A
Issued: 6/94 • Retired: 1/96
Market Value:
A. New Face (1/95-1/96) ③–**$2,000** ②–**$2,100**
B. Old Face (6/94-1/95) ②–**$1,900** ①–**$2,000**

BEANIE BABIES®

	Date Purchased	Tag Gen.	Price Paid	Value of My Collection
131.				
132.				
133.				
134.				
135.				
PENCIL TOTALS				

136

B

A

Teddy™ (magenta)
10" • Bear • #4056 • Born: N/A
Issued: 6/94 • Retired: 1/96
Market Value:
A. New Face (1/95-1/96) ❸–$2,000 ❷–$2,100
B. Old Face (6/94-1/95) ❷–$1,900 ❶–$2,000

137

A

B

Teddy™ (teal)
10" • Bear • #4051 • Born: N/A
Issued: 6/94 • Retired: 1/96
Market Value:
A. New Face (1/95-1/96) ❸–$2,050 ❷–$2,150
B. Old Face (6/94-1/95) ❷–$1,900 ❶–$2,000

138

B

A

C

Teddy™ (violet)
10" • Bear • #4055 • Born: N/A
Issued: 6/94 • Retired: 1/96
Market Value:
A. New Face (1/95-1/96)
❸–$2,150 ❷–$2,050
B. New Face/Employee Bear w/Red
Tush Tag (Green or Red Ribbon)
No Hang Tag – $4,000
C. Old Face (6/94-1/95)
❷–$1,900 ❶–$2,000

139

New!

Tracker™
9" • Basset Hound • #4198 • Born: 6/5/97
Issued: 5/98 • Current
Market Value: ❺–$_____

BEANIE BABIES®

	Date Purchased	Tag Gen.	Price Paid	Value of My Collection
136.				
137.				
138.				
139.				
140.				
✏ PENCIL TOTALS				

140

Trap™
9" • Mouse • #4042 • Born: N/A
Issued: 6/94 • Retired: 6/95
Market Value: ❸–$1,575
❷–$1,650 ❶–$1,700

(141)

Tuffy™
10" • Terrier • #4108 • Born: 10/12/96
Issued: 5/97 • Current
Market Value: ⑤-$_____ ④-$14

(142)

B

Tuck™ style 4076
DATE OF BIRTH : 9 - 18 - 95
Tusk brushes his teeth everyday
To keep them shiny, it's the only way
Teeth are special, so you must try
To sparkle when you say 'HI'!
Visit our web page!!!
http://www.ty.com

Tusk™
8" • Walrus • #4076 • Born: 9/18/95
Issued: Est. 6/95 • Retired: 1/97
Market Value:
A. "Tusk™" Swing Tag (6/95-1/97)
④-$145 ③-$225
B. "Tuck™" Swing Tag (Est. Early 96-1/97) ④-$175

(143)

Twigs™
9" • Giraffe • #4068 • Born: 5/19/95
Issued: 1/96 • Retired: 5/98
Market Value: ⑤-$25 ④-$35 ③-$125

(144)

Valentino™
10" • Bear • #4058 • Born: 2/14/94
Issued: 1/95 • Current
Market Value: ⑤-$_____ ④-$33
③-$125 ②-$240

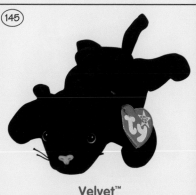

(145)

Velvet™
10" • Panther • #4064 • Born: 12/16/95
Issued: 6/95 • Retired: 10/97
Market Value: ④-$38 ③-$125

BEANIE BABIES®

	Date Purchased	Tag Gen.	Price Paid	Value of My Collection
141.				
142.				
143.				
144.				
145.				
✏ PENCIL TOTALS				

(146)

Waddle™
10" • Penguin • #4075 • Born: 12/19/95
Issued: 6/95 • Retired: 5/98
Market Value: ⑤–**$23** ④–**$30** ③–**$115**

(147)

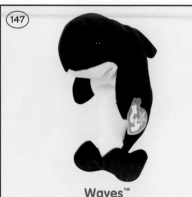

Waves™
10" • Whale • #4084 • Born: 12/8/96
Issued: 5/97 • Retired: 5/98
Market Value: ⑤–**$23** ④–**$32**

(148)

Web™
10" • Spider • #4041 • Born: N/A
Issued: 6/94 • Retired: 1/96
Market Value: ③–**$1,500**
②–**$1,650** ①–**$1,750**

(149)

Weenie™
9" • Dachshund • #4013 • Born: 7/20/95
Issued: 1/96 • Retired: 5/98
Market Value: ⑤–**$30** ④–**$38** ③–**$120**

BEANIE BABIES®

	Date Purchased	Tag Gen.	Price Paid	Value of My Collection
146.				
147.				
148.				
149.				
150.				
✏ PENCIL TOTALS				

(150)

New!

Whisper™
8" • Deer • #4194 • Born: 4/5/97
Issued: 5/98 • Current
Market Value: ⑤–$_____

151

New!

Wise™
9" • Owl • #4187 • Born: 5/31/97
Issued: 5/98 • Current
Market Value: ⑤–$_____

152

Wrinkles™
10" • Bulldog • #4103 • Born: 5/1/96
Issued: 6/96 • Retired: 9/98
Market Value: ⑤–$15 ④–$22

153

Ziggy™
10" • Zebra • #4063 • Born: 12/24/95
Issued: 6/95 • Retired: 5/98
Market Value: ⑤–$22 ④–$30 ③–$125

154

A

B

C

Zip™
10" • Cat • #4004 • Born: 3/28/94
Issued: 1/95 • Retired: 5/98
Market Value:
A. White Paws (3/96-5/98)
⑤–$47 ④–$55 ③–$575
B. All Black (1/96-3/96)
③–$2,100
C. White Face (1/95-1/96)
③–$575 ②–$600

BEANIE BABIES®

	Date Purchased	Tag Gen.	Price Paid	Value of My Collection
151.				
152.				
153.				
154.				
PENCIL TOTALS				

VALUE GUIDE — BEANIE BABIES®

SPORTS PROMOTION BEANIE BABIES®

Here's a rundown of some of the special *Beanie Babies* sports promotions announced through September 1998.

(1)
Baldy™
Philadelphia 76ers
1/17/98 • LE-5,000
Market Value: $230

(2)
Batty™
Milwaukee Brewers
5/31/98 • LE-12,000
Market Value: $115

(3)
Batty™
New York Mets
7/12/98 • LE-30,000
Market Value: $125

(4)
Blackie™
Boston Bruins
10/12/98 • LE-5,000
Market Value: N/E

(5)
Blackie™
Chicago Bears
In Club Kits • LE-20,000
Market Value: N/E

(6)
Blackie™
Chicago Bears
11/8/98 • LE-8,000
Market Value: N/E

(7)
Blizzard™
Chicago White Sox
7/12/98 • LE-20,000
Market Value: $160

(8)
Bones™
New York Yankees
3/10/98 • N/A
Market Value: $245

(9)
Bongo™
Charlotte Sting
7/17/98 • LE-3,000
Market Value: $170

(10)
Bongo™
Cleveland Cavaliers
4/5/98 • LE-5,000
Market Value: $150

SPORTS PROMOTION BEANIE BABIES®

	Price Paid	Value of My Collection
1.		
2.		
3.		
4.		
5.		
6.		
7.		
8.		
9.		
10.		
11.		
12.		
13.		
14.		
15.		
16.		
17.		
18.		
19.		
20.		
21.		
22.		
23.		
24.		
25.		
26.		
27.		
28.		

✎ PENCIL TOTALS

(11)
Chip™
Atlanta Braves
8/19/98 • LE-12,000
Market Value: $120

(12)
Chocolate™
Dallas Cowboys
9/6/98 • LE-10,000
Market Value: N/E

(13)
Chocolate™
Denver Nuggets
4/17/98 • LE-5,000
Market Value: $155

(14)
Chocolate™
Seattle Mariners
9/5/98 • LE-10,000
Market Value: N/E

(15)
Cubbie™
Chicago Cubs
1/16-1/18/98 • LE-100
Market Value: N/E

(16)
Cubbie™
Chicago Cubs
5/18/97 • LE-10,000
Market Value: $215

(17)
Cubbie™
Chicago Cubs
9/6/97 • LE-10,000
Market Value: N/E

(18)
Curly™
Charlotte Sting
6/15/98 • LE-5,000
Market Value: $220

(19)
Curly™
Chicago Bears
12/20/98 • LE-10,000
Market Value: N/E

(20)
Curly™
Cleveland Rockers
8/15/98 • LE-3,200
Market Value: $150

(21)
Curly™
New York Mets
8/22/98 • LE-30,000
Market Value: N/E

(22)
Curly™
San Antonio Spurs
4/27/98 • LE-2,500
Market Value: $210

(23)
Daisy™
Chicago Cubs
5/3/98 • LE-10,000
Market Value: $430

(24)
Derby™
Houston Astros
8/16/98 • LE-15,000
Market Value: $120

(25)
Dotty™
Los Angeles Sparks
7/31/98 • LE-3,000
Market Value: $185

(26)
Ears™
Oakland A's
3/15/98 • LE-1,500
Market Value: $475

(27)
Glory™
All-Star Game
7/7/98 • LE-52,000 approx.
Market Value: $350

(28)
Gobbles™
St. Louis Blues
11/24/98 • LE-7,500
Market Value: N/E

 Canadian Special Olympics

 Major League Baseball

 National Basketball Association

29 · Gracie™
Chicago Cubs
9/13/98 • LE-10,000
Market Value: N/E

30 · Hissy™
Arizona Diamondbacks
6/14/98 • LE-6,500
Market Value: $170

31 · Lucky™
Minnesota Twins
7/31/98 • LE-10,000
Market Value: $120

32 · Maple™
Canadian Special Olympics
8/97 & 12/97 • N/A
Market Value: $540

33 · Mel™
Anaheim Angels
9/6/98 • LE-10,000
Market Value: N/E

34 · Mel™
Detroit Shock
7/25/98 • LE-5,000
Market Value: $130

35 · Mystic™
Los Angeles Sparks
8/3/98 • LE-5,000
Market Value: $140

36 · Mystic™
Washington Mystics
7/11/98 • LE-5,000
Market Value: $180

37 · Peanut™
Oakland A's
8/1/98 • LE-15,000
Market Value: $160

38 · Peanut™
Oakland A's
9/6/98 • LE-15,000
Market Value: N/E

39 · Pinky™
San Antonio Spurs
4/29/98 • LE-2,500
Market Value: $210

40 · Pinky™
Tampa Bay Devil Rays
8/23/98 • LE-10,000
Market Value: $100

41 · Pugsly™
Atlanta Braves
9/2/98 • LE-12,000
Market Value: N/E

42 · Pugsly™
Texas Rangers
8/4/98 • LE-10,000
Market Value: $195

43 · Roary™
Kansas City Royals
5/31/98 • LE-13,000
Market Value: $160

44 · Rocket™
Toronto Blue Jays
9/6/98 • LE-12,000
Market Value: N/E

45 · Rover™
Cincinnati Reds
8/16/98 • LE-15,000
Market Value: $120

46 · Scoop™
Houston Comets
8/6/98 • LE-5,000
Market Value: $230

47 · Sly™
Arizona Diamondbacks
8/27/98 • LE-10,000
Market Value: N/E

48 · Smoochy™
St. Louis Cardinals
8/14/98 • LE-20,000
Market Value: $110

49 · Stretch™
New York Yankees
8/9/98 • N/A
Market Value: $110

50 · Stretch™
St. Louis Cardinals
5/22/98 • LE-20,000
Market Value: $180

51 · Stripes™
Detroit Tigers
5/31/98 • LE-10,000
Market Value: $130

52 · Stripes™
Detroit Tigers
8/8/98 • LE-10,000
Market Value: $145

53 · Strut™
Indiana Pacers
4/2/98 • LE-5,000
Market Value: $160

54 · Tuffy™
San Francisco Giants
8/30/98 • LE-10,000
Market Value: N/E

55 · Valentino™
Canadian Special Olympics
6/98, 9/98 & 10/98 • N/A
Market Value: $300

56 · Valentino™
New York Yankees
5/17/98 • LE-10,000
Market Value: $425

57 · Weenie™
Tampa Bay Devil Rays
7/26/98 • LE-15,000
Market Value: $150

SPORTS PROMOTION BEANIE BABIES®

	Price Paid	Value of My Collection
29.		
30.		
31.		
32.		
33.		
34.		
35.		
36.		
37.		
38.		
39.		
40.		
41.		
42.		
43.		
44.		
45.		
46.		
47.		
48.		
49.		
50.		
51.		
52.		
53.		
54.		
55.		
56.		
57.		

PENCIL TOTALS

BEANIE BABIES®

 National Football League
 National Hockey League
 Women's National Basketball Association

An Appetite For Teenie Beanie Babies™

No one could have imagined the collecting feeding frenzy that was to occur with the debut of the McDonald's *Teenie Beanie Babies* promotion. The first promotion in April 1997 featured ten designs which sold out in less than a week in many areas of the country. Ty and McDonald's teamed up again in May 1998 with 12 more designs that were snatched up quickly by hungry collectors. Designed to resemble their larger *Beanie Babies* counterparts, these tiny critters are lovable enough to fulfill even the largest of appetites.

1 New!

Bones™
6" • Dog • 2nd Promotion, #9 of 12
Issued: 5/98 • Retired: 6/98
Market Value: $12

2 New!

Bongo™
5" • Monkey • 2nd Promotion, #2 of 12
Issued: 5/98 • Retired: 6/98
Market Value: $17

Teenie Beanie Babies™

	Date Purchased	Price Paid	Value of My Collection
1.			
2.			
3.			
PENCIL TOTALS			

3

Chocolate™
5.5" • Moose • 1st Promotion, #4 of 10
Issued: 4/97 • Retired: 5/97
Market Value: $35

(4)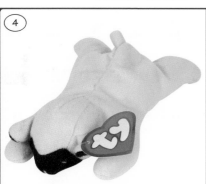

Chops™
5" • Lamb • 1st Promotion, #3 of 10
Issued: 4/97 • Retired: 5/97
Market Value: $43

(5) New! ✓

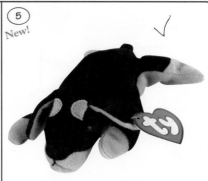

Doby™
4.5" • Doberman • 2nd Promotion, #1 of 12
Issued: 5/98 • Retired: 6/98
Market Value: $17

(6)

Goldie™
4.5" • Goldfish • 1st Promotion, #5 of 10
Issued: 4/97 • Retired: 5/97
Market Value: $32

(7) New! ✓

Happy™
6" • Hippo • 2nd Promotion, #6 of 12
Issued: 5/98 • Retired: 6/98
Market Value: $10

(8) New! ✓

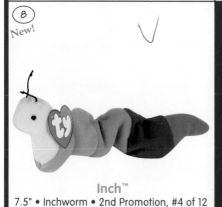

Inch™
7.5" • Inchworm • 2nd Promotion, #4 of 12
Issued: 5/98 • Retired: 6/98
Market Value: $10

TEENIE BEANIE BABIES™

	Date Purchased	Price Paid	Value of My Collection
4.			
5.			
6.			
7.			
8.			
✎ PENCIL TOTALS			

TEENIE BEANIE BABIES™

⑨

Lizz™
8" • Lizard • 1st Promotion, #10 of 10
Issued: 4/97 • Retired: 5/97
Market Value: $27

⑩ New!

Mel™
5" • Koala • 2nd Promotion, #7 of 12
Issued: 5/98 • Retired: 6/98
Market Value: $10

⑪

Patti™
5.5" • Platypus • 1st Promotion, #1 of 10
Issued: 4/97 • Retired: 5/97
Market Value: $48

⑫ New!

Peanut™
6" • Elephant • 2nd Promotion, #12 of 12
Issued: 5/98 • Retired: 6/98
Market Value: $12

TEENIE BEANIE BABIES™

	Date Purchased	Price Paid	Value of My Collection
9.			
10.			
11.			
12.			
13.			
✏ PENCIL TOTALS			

⑬ New!

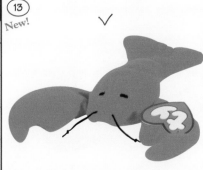

Pinchers™
6.5" • Lobster • 2nd Promotion, #5 of 12
Issued: 5/98 • Retired: 6/98
Market Value: $10

(14)

Pinky™
7" • Flamingo • 1st Promotion, #2 of 10
Issued: 4/97 • Retired: 5/97
Market Value: $55

(15)

Quacks™
3.5" • Duck • 1st Promotion, #9 of 10
Issued: 4/97 • Retired: 5/97
Market Value: $24

(16) New!

Scoop™
4" • Pelican • 2nd Promotion, #8 of 12
Issued: 5/98 • Retired: 6/98
Market Value: $10

(17)

Seamore™
4.5" • Seal • 1st Promotion, #7 of 10
Issued: 4/97 • Retired: 5/97
Market Value: $33

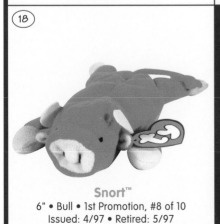

(18)

Snort™
6" • Bull • 1st Promotion, #8 of 10
Issued: 4/97 • Retired: 5/97
Market Value: $24

TEENIE BEANIE BABIES™

	Date Purchased	Price Paid	Value of My Collection
14.			
15.			
16.			
17.			
18.			
PENCIL TOTALS			

TEENIE BEANIE BABIES™

19

Speedy™
4" • Turtle • 1st Promotion, #6 of 10
Issued: 4/97 • Retired: 5/97
Market Value: $32

20

New!

Twigs™
6" • Giraffe • 2nd Promotion, #3 of 12
Issued: 5/98 • Retired: 6/98
Market Value: $15

21

New!

Waddle™
5" • Penguin • 2nd Promotion, #11 of 12
Issued: 5/98 • Retired: 6/98
Market Value: $12

22

New!

Zip™
5" • Cat • 2nd Promotion, #10 of 12
Issued: 5/98 • Retired: 6/98
Market Value: $12

TEENIE BEANIE BABIES™

	Date Purchased	Price Paid	Value of My Collection
19.			
20.			
21.			
22.			
✏ PENCIL TOTALS			

(23)

1997 Teenie Beanie Babies™ Complete Set (set/10)
Issued: 4/97 • Retired: 5/97
Market Value: $295

(24)

New!

1998 Teenie Beanie Babies™ Complete Set (set/12)
Issued: 5/98 • Retired: 6/98
Market Value: $110

TEENIE BEANIE BABIES™

	Date Purchased	Price Paid	Value of My Collection
23.			
24.			
PENCIL TOTALS			

TEENIE BEANIE BABIES™

PILLOW PALS™ - FUN FOR ALL AGES

With the debut of the *Pillow Pals* in 1995, Ty expanded its appeal once again, this time into the realm of the baby-friendly market. With embroidered features which are 100% machine washable, these fluffy pals are designed with the safety of small children in mind. In three years, the collection has expanded to 27 animals, 20 of which are still current. In 1998, nine new critters were introduced while five were retired.

1

Ba Ba™
15" • Lamb • #3008
Issued: 1997 • Current
Market Value: $_____

2

Bruiser™
14" • Bulldog • #3018
Issued: 1997 • Current
Market Value: $_____

PILLOW PALS™

	Date Purchased	Price Paid	Value of My Collection
1.			
2.			
3.			
PENCIL TOTALS			

3

Carrots™
15" • Bunny • #3010
Issued: 1997 • Current
Market Value: $_____

4 New!

Clover™
15" • Rabbit • #3020
Issued: 1998 • Current
Market Value: $_____

5 New!

Foxy™
19" • Fox • #3022
Issued: 1998 • Current
Market Value: $_____

6 New!

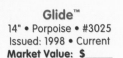

Glide™
14" • Porpoise • #3025
Issued: 1998 • Current
Market Value: $_____

7

Huggy™
14" • Bear • #3002
Issued: 1995 • Retired: 1998
A. Pink Ribbon (1997-98)
B. Blue Ribbon (1995-97)
Market Value: A/B–$30

8

Meow™
15" • Cat • #3011
Issued: 1997 • Current
A. Tan (1997-Current)
B. Gray (1997)
Market Value: A–$_____   B–$110

PILLOW PALS™

	Date Purchased	Price Paid	Value of My Collection
4.			
5.			
6.			
7.			
8.			
PENCIL TOTALS			

PILLOW PALS™

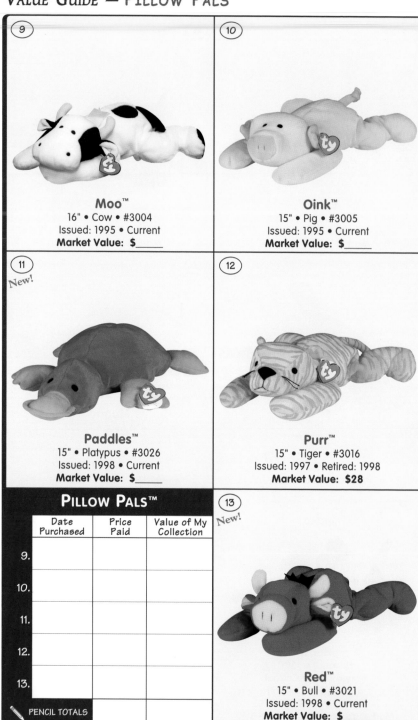

9

Moo™
16" • Cow • #3004
Issued: 1995 • Current
Market Value: $_____

10

Oink™
15" • Pig • #3005
Issued: 1995 • Current
Market Value: $_____

11
New!

Paddles™
15" • Platypus • #3026
Issued: 1998 • Current
Market Value: $_____

12

Purr™
15" • Tiger • #3016
Issued: 1997 • Retired: 1998
Market Value: $28

PILLOW PALS™

	Date Purchased	Price Paid	Value of My Collection
9.			
10.			
11.			
12.			
13.			
PENCIL TOTALS			

13
New!

Red™
15" • Bull • #3021
Issued: 1998 • Current
Market Value: $_____

14

Ribbit™
14" • Frog • #3006
Issued: 1995 • Retired: 1996
Market Value: $375

15

Ribbit™
14" • Frog • #3009
Issued: 1997 • Current
Market Value: $_____

16
New!

Sherbet™
15" • Bear • #3027
Issued: 1998 • Current
Market Value: $_____

17

Snap™
14" • Turtle • #3007
Issued: 1995 • Retired: 1996
Market Value: $365

18

Snap™
14" • Turtle • #3015
Issued: 1997 • Retired: 1998
Market Value: $30

Pillow Pals™

	Date Purchased	Price Paid	Value of My Collection
14.			
15.			
16.			
17.			
18.			
PENCIL TOTALS			

Pillow Pals™

19

Snuggy™
14" • Bear • #3001
Issued: 1995 • Retired: 1998
A. Blue Ribbon (1997-98)
B. Pink Ribbon (1995-97)
Market Value: A/B–$30

20

Speckles™
15" • Leopard • #3017
Issued: 1997 • Current
Market Value: $_____

21

New!

Spotty™
15" • Dalmatian • #3019
Issued: 1998 • Current
Market Value: $_____

22

Squirt™
15" • Elephant • #3013
Issued: 1997 • Current
Market Value: $_____

PILLOW PALS™

	Date Purchased	Price Paid	Value of My Collection
19.			
20.			
21.			
22.			
23.			
✏ PENCIL TOTALS			

23

New!

Swinger™
15" • Monkey • #3023
Issued: 1998 • Current
Market Value: $_____

(24)
New!

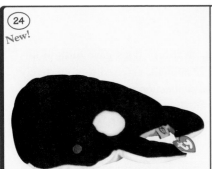

Tide™
14" • Whale • #3024
Issued: 1998 • Current
Market Value: $_____

(25)

Tubby™
15" • Hippo • #3012
Issued: 1997 • Current
Market Value: $_____

(26)

Woof™
15" • Dog • #3003
Issued: 1995 • Current
Market Value: $_____

(27)

Zulu™
15" • Zebra • #3014
Issued: 1997 • Retired: 1998
A. Thick Stripes (1997-98)
B. Thin Stripes (1997)
Market Value: A–$35 B–$70

PILLOW PALS™

	Date Purchased	Price Paid	Value of My Collection
24.			
25.			
26.			
27.			
✏ PENCIL TOTALS			

PILLOW PALS™

107

THE WONDERFUL WORLD OF TY® PLUSH

In 1986, a small litter of cats and a trio of dogs gave birth to this menagerie of 357 animals, referred to collectively as *Ty Plush*. This collection is divided into distinct groups, which are listed separately in the value guide in the following order: Bears, Cats, Dogs, Country and Wildlife.

Today, only 77 of these adorable creatures are current. There were 19 new introductions in 1998, as well as two retirements.

①

1991 Ty Collectable Bear™
21" • Bear • #5500
Issued: 1991 • Retired: 1991
Market Value: $1,000

②

1992 Ty Collectable Bear™
21" • Bear • #5500
Issued: 1992 • Retired: 1992
A. "1992 Ty Collectable Bear™" Version
B. "Edmond™" Version
Market Value: A–$500 B–N/E

BEARS

	Date Purchased	Price Paid	Value of My Collection
1.			
2.			
3.			

✎ PENCIL TOTALS

③

1997 Holiday Bear™
14" • Bear • #5700
Issued: 1997 • Retired: 1997
Market Value: $50

(4)

Aurora™
13" • Polar Bear • #5103
Issued: 1996 • Retired: 1997
Market Value: $48

(5)

Baby Buddy™
20" • Bear • #5011
Issued: 1992 • Retired: 1992
Market Value: $470

(6)

Baby Cinnamon™
13" • Bear • #5105
Issued: 1996 • Retired: 1996
Market Value: $45

(7)

Baby Curly™
12" • Bear • #5017
Issued: 1993 • Retired: 1997
Market Value: $37

(8)

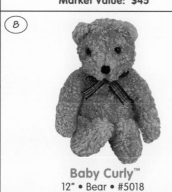

Baby Curly™
12" • Bear • #5018
Issued: 1993 • Current
A. Ribbon (1993-Current)
B. Sweater (1998)
Market Value: A–$_____ B–N/E

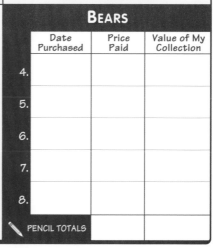

BEARS

	Date Purchased	Price Paid	Value of My Collection
4.			
5.			
6.			
7.			
8.			
PENCIL TOTALS			

BEARS

9

Baby Ginger™
14" • Bear • #5108
Issued: 1997 • Current
Market Value: $_____

10

Baby Paws™
12" • Bear • #5110
Issued: 1997 • Current
Market Value: $_____

11

Baby Paws™
12" • Bear • #5111
Issued: 1997 • Current
Market Value: $_____

12

New!

Baby Paws™
12" • Bear • #5112
Issued: 1998 • Current
Market Value: $_____

BEARS

	Date Purchased	Price Paid	Value of My Collection
9.			
10.			
11.			
12.			
13.			
✏ PENCIL TOTALS			

13

Baby PJ™
12" • Bear • #5016
Issued: 1993 • Current
Market Value: $_____

(14)

Baby PJ™
12" • Bear • #5100
Issued: 1994 • Retired: 1994
Market Value: $75

(15)

Baby Powder™
14" • Bear • #5109
Issued: 1997 • Current
Market Value: $_____

(16)

Baby Spice™
13" • Bear • #5104
Issued: 1996 • Retired: 1997
A. "Baby Spice™" Swing Tag
B. "ByBy Spice™" Swing Tag
Market Value: A/B–$35

(17)

Bailey™
19" • Bear • #5502
Issued: 1997 • Retired: 1997
Market Value: $45

(18)

Bamboo™
13" • Panda • #5106
Issued: 1996 • Retired: 1997
Market Value: $45

BEARS

	Date Purchased	Price Paid	Value of My Collection
14.			
15.			
16.			
17.			
18.			
PENCIL TOTALS			

BEARS

19 New!

Bamboo™
12" • Panda • #5113
Issued: 1998 • Current
Market Value: $_____

20

Baron™
18" • Bear • #5200
Issued: 1995 • Retired: 1995
Market Value: $85

21

Beanie Bear™
12" • Bear • #5000
Issued: 1988 • Retired: 1990
Market Value: $815

22

Beanie Bear™
12" • Bear • #5100
Issued: 1991 • Retired: 1992
Market Value: $815

BEARS

	Date Purchased	Price Paid	Value of My Collection
19.			
20.			
21.			
22.			
23.			
PENCIL TOTALS			

23

Beanie Bear™
12" • Bear • #5101
Issued: 1991 • Retired: 1991
Market Value: N/E

Beanie Bear™
12" • Bear • #5102
Issued: 1991 • Retired: 1991
Market Value: N/E

Big Beanie Bear™
15" • Bear • #5011
Issued: 1990 • Retired: 1990
Market Value: $800

Big Beanie Bear™
15" • Bear • #5200
Issued: 1991 • Retired: 1991
Market Value: $800

Big Beanie Bear™
15" • Bear • #5201
Issued: 1991 • Retired: 1991
Market Value: N/E

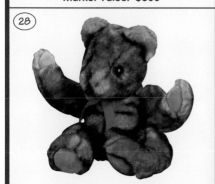

Big Beanie Bear™
15" • Bear • #5202
Issued: 1991 • Retired: 1991
Market Value: $800

BEARS

	Date Purchased	Price Paid	Value of My Collection
24.			
25.			
26.			
27.			
28.			
✎ PENCIL TOTALS			

BEARS

(29)

Big Pudgy™
28" • Bear • #9006
Issued: 1994 • Retired: 1996
Market Value: $220

(30)

Big Shaggy™
26" • Bear • #9015
Issued: 1992 • Retired: 1992
Market Value: $325

(31)

Blackie™
13" • Bear • #5003
Issued: 1988 • Retired: 1990
Market Value: $540

(32)

Brownie™
13" • Bear • #5100
Issued: 1996 • Retired: 1996
Market Value: $66

Bears

	Date Purchased	Price Paid	Value of My Collection
29.			
30.			
31.			
32.			
33.			
PENCIL TOTALS			

(33)

Buddy™
20" • Bear • #5007
Issued: 1990 • Retired: 1992
Market Value: $510

(34)

Buddy™
20" • Bear • #5019
Issued: 1993 • Retired: 1996
Market Value: $52

(35)

Cinnamon™
13" • Bear • #5004
Issued: 1989 • Retired: 1990
Market Value: $730

(36)

Cinnamon™
18" • Bear • #5021
Issued: 1996 • Retired: 1996
Market Value: $52

(37)

Cocoa™
12" • Bear • #5107
Issued: 1997 • Current
Market Value: $_____

BEARS

	Date Purchased	Price Paid	Value of My Collection
34.			
35.			
36.			
37.			
✎ PENCIL TOTALS			

BEARS

38

Curly™
18" • Bear • #5300
Issued: 1991 • Retired: 1997
A. 18" (1993-97)
B. 22" (1991-92)
Market Value: A/B–$45

39

Curly™
22" • Bear • #5301
Issued: 1991 • Retired: 1991
Market Value: N/E

40

Curly™
18" • Bear • #5302
Issued: 1991 • Current
A. 18"/Ribbon (1993-Current)
B. 18"/Sweater (1998)
C. 22" (1991-92)
Market Value: A–$_____ B–N/E C–N/E

41

Cuzzy™
13" • Bear • #5203
Issued: 1996 • Retired: 1997
Market Value: $94

BEARS

	Date Purchased	Price Paid	Value of My Collection
38.			
39.			
40.			
41.			
42.			
✏ PENCIL TOTALS			

42

Dumpling™
12" • Bear • #5022
Issued: 1996 • Retired: 1996
Market Value: $57

(43)

Dumpling™
12" • Bear • #5023
Issued: 1996 • Retired: 1996
Market Value: $57

(44)

Eleanor™
19" • Bear • #5500
Issued: 1996 • Retired: 1997
Market Value: $50

(45)

Faith™
10" • Bear • #5600
Issued: 1996 • Current
Market Value: $_____

(46)
New!

Forest™
12" • Bear • #5114
Issued: 1998 • Current
Market Value: $_____

	Date Purchased	Price Paid	Value of My Collection
BEARS			
43.			
44.			
45.			
46.			
PENCIL TOTALS			

BEARS

47

Fuzzy™
13" • Bear • #5204
Issued: 1996 • Retired: 1997
Market Value: $85

48

Ginger™
18" • Bear • #5306
Issued: 1997 • Retired: 1997
Market Value: $43

49

Honey™
14" • Bear • #5004
Issued: 1991 • Retired: 1994
A. Blue Ribbon (1992-94)
B. Red Ribbon (1991)
Market Value: A/B–$160

50

Hope™
10" • Bear • #5601
Issued: 1996 • Current
Market Value: $_____

BEARS

	Date Purchased	Price Paid	Value of My Collection
47.			
48.			
49.			
50.			
51.			
✏ PENCIL TOTALS			

51

Jumbo PJ™
40" • Bear • #9016
Issued: 1994 • Retired: 1994
Market Value: N/E

(52)

Jumbo PJ™
40" • Bear • #9020
Issued: 1992 • Current
Market Value: $_____

(53)

Jumbo Pumpkin™
40" • Bear • #9017
Issued: 1995 • Retired: 1996
Market Value: N/E

(54)

Jumbo Rumples™
40" • Bear • #9016
Issued: 1995 • Retired: 1996
Market Value: $160

(55)

Jumbo Shaggy™
40" • Bear • #9016
Issued: 1992 • Retired: 1993
Market Value: $350

(56)

Jumbo Shaggy™
40" • Bear • #9017
Issued: 1992 • Retired: 1994
Market Value: $350

BEARS

	Date Purchased	Price Paid	Value of My Collection
52.			
53.			
54.			
55.			
56.			
✏ PENCIL TOTALS			

BEARS

119

57

Jumbo Shaggy™
40" • Bear • #9026
Issued: 1993 • Retired: 1996
Market Value: $350

58

Kasey™
20" • Koala • #5006
Issued: 1989 • Retired: 1991
A. 20"/Gray (1990-91)
B. 13"/Brown (1989)
Market Value: A–$750 B–$825

59

Large Curly™
26" • Bear • #9018
Issued: 1992 • Retired: 1997
Market Value: $85

60

Large Curly™
26" • Bear • #9019
Issued: 1992 • Current
Market Value: $_____

BEARS

	Date Purchased	Price Paid	Value of My Collection
57.			
58.			
59.			
60.			
61.			
✏ PENCIL TOTALS			

61

Large Ginger™
22" • Bear • #9027
Issued: 1997 • Retired: 1997
Market Value: $70

62

Large Honey™
26" • Bear • #9021
Issued: 1992 • Retired: 1994
Market Value: $240

63

Large McGee™
26" • Bear • #9005
Issued: 1992 • Retired: 1997
Market Value: $70

64

Large Moonbeam™
20" • Bear • #9009
Issued: 1995 • Retired: 1995
Market Value: $210

65

Large Paws™
28" • Bear • #9029
Issued: 1997 • Current
Market Value: $_____

66

Large Paws™
28" • Bear • #9030
Issued: 1997 • Current
Market Value: $_____

BEARS

	Date Purchased	Price Paid	Value of My Collection
62.			
63.			
64.			
65.			
66.			
✏ PENCIL TOTALS			

BEARS

121

67
New!

Large Paws™
28" • Bear • #9031
Issued: 1998 • Current
Market Value: $_____

68

Large Ping Pong™
26" • Panda • #9010
Issued: 1992 • Retired: 1993
Market Value: $450

69

Large PJ™
26" • Bear • #9012
Issued: 1992 • Current
A. 26" (1993-Current)
B. 24" (1992)
Market Value: A–$_____ B–N/E

70

Large PJ™
26" • Bear • #9014
Issued: 1994 • Retired: 1994
Market Value: $180

Bears

	Date Purchased	Price Paid	Value of My Collection
67.			
68.			
69.			
70.			
71.			
PENCIL TOTALS			

71

Large Powder™
22" • Bear • #9028
Issued: 1997 • Retired: 1997
Market Value: $80

(72)

Large Pumpkin™
26" • Bear • #9015
Issued: 1995 • Retired: 1996
Market Value: $180

(73)

Large Rumples™
26" • Bear • #9000
Issued: 1995 • Retired: 1995
Market Value: $190

(74)

Large Rumples™
26" • Bear • #9002
Issued: 1995 • Retired: 1996
Market Value: $110

(75)

Large Scruffy™
28" • Bear • #9000
Issued: 1992 • Retired: 1993
Market Value: $190

(76)

Large Scruffy™
28" • Bear • #9013
Issued: 1992 • Retired: 1992
Market Value: $325

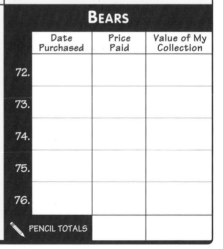

	Date Purchased	Price Paid	Value of My Collection
BEARS			
72.			
73.			
74.			
75.			
76.			
✏ PENCIL TOTALS			

BEARS

77

Large Shaggy™
26" • Bear • #9014
Issued: 1992 • Retired: 1993
Market Value: $310

78

Large Shaggy™
26" • Bear • #9015
Issued: 1993 • Retired: 1994
Market Value: $310

79

Large Shaggy™
26" • Bear • #9025
Issued: 1993 • Retired: 1996
Market Value: $160

80

Large Snowball™
26" • Bear • #9009
Issued: 1992 • Retired: 1993
Market Value: $250

BEARS

	Date Purchased	Price Paid	Value of My Collection
77.			
78.			
79.			
80.			
✏ PENCIL TOTALS			

⑧¹

Lazy™
20" • Bear • #5008
Issued: 1995 • Retired: 1996
Market Value: $60

⑧² New!

Magee™
10" • Bear • #5027
Issued: 1998 • Current
Market Value: $_____

⑧³

Mandarin™
13" • Panda • #5201
Issued: 1996 • Retired: 1997
Market Value: $115

⑧⁴

McGee™
14" • Bear • #5001
Issued: 1988 • Retired: 1997
A. 14" (1991-97)
B. 13" (1988-90)
Market Value: A–$65 B–$700

⑧⁵

Midnight™
20" • Bear • #5009
Issued: 1990 • Retired: 1993
A. Black & Brown (1991, 1993)
B. All Black (1990)
Market Value: A/B–$340

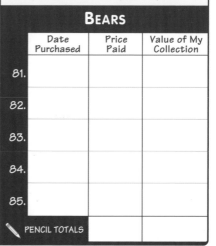

BEARS

	Date Purchased	Price Paid	Value of My Collection
81.			
82.			
83.			
84.			
85.			
✏ PENCIL TOTALS			

BEARS

(86)

Midnight™
13" • Bear • #5101
Issued: 1996 • Retired: 1996
Market Value: $65

(87)

Moonbeam™
14" • Bear • #5009
Issued: 1995 • Retired: 1995
Market Value: $165

(88)

Nutmeg™
18" • Bear • #5013
Issued: 1996 • Retired: 1997
Market Value: $58

(89)

Oreo™
20" • Panda • #5005
Issued: 1994 • Retired: 1996
Market Value: $83

BEARS

	Date Purchased	Price Paid	Value of My Collection
86.			
87.			
88.			
89.			
90.			
PENCIL TOTALS			

(90)

Oreo™
20" • Panda • #5010
Issued: 1990 • Retired: 1991
Market Value: $280

(91)

Papa PJ™
50" • Bear • #9021
Issued: 1997 • Current
Market Value: $_____

(92)

Papa Pumpkin™
50" • Bear • #9023
Issued: 1995 • Retired: 1996
Market Value: $1,100

(93)

Papa Rumples™
50" • Bear • #9022
Issued: 1995 • Retired: 1996
Market Value: $980

(94)

Papa Shaggy™
50" • Bear • #9024
Issued: 1994 • Retired: 1996
Market Value: $950

(95)

Paws™
18" • Bear • #5024
Issued: 1997 • Current
Market Value: $_____

BEARS

	Date Purchased	Price Paid	Value of My Collection
91.			
92.			
93.			
94.			
95.			
✏ PENCIL TOTALS			

BEARS

(96)

Paws™
18" • Bear • #5025
Issued: 1997 • Current
Market Value: $_____

(97)

New!

Paws™
18" • Bear • #5026
Issued: 1998 • Current
Market Value: $_____

(98)

Ping Pong™
14" • Panda • #5005
Issued: 1989 • Retired: 1993
A. 14" (1991-93)
B. 13" (1989-90)
Market Value: A–$350 B–N/E

(99)

*photo
not
available*

Ping Pong™
N/A • Panda • #5007
Issued: 1989 • Retired: 1989
Market Value: N/E

BEARS

	Date Purchased	Price Paid	Value of My Collection
96.			
97.			
98.			
99.			
100.			
✏ PENCIL TOTALS			

(100)

PJ™
18" • Bear • #5200
Issued: 1994 • Retired: 1994
Market Value: $170

(101)

PJ™
18" • Bear • #5400
Issued: 1991 • Current
A. 18" (1993-Current)
B. 22" (1991-92)
Market Value: A–$_____ B–N/E

(102)

Powder™
18" • Bear • #5307
Issued: 1997 • Retired: 1997
Market Value: $76

(103)

Prayer Bear™
14" • Bear • #5600
Issued: 1992 • Retired: 1994
Market Value: $250

(104)

Prayer Bear™
14" • Bear • #5601
Issued: 1992 • Retired: 1993
Market Value: $285

(105)

Pudgy™
14" • Bear • #5006
Issued: 1994 • Retired: 1996
Market Value: $145

BEARS

	Date Purchased	Price Paid	Value of My Collection
101.			
102.			
103.			
104.			
105.			
PENCIL TOTALS			

BEARS

(106)

Pumpkin™
18" • Bear • #5304
Issued: 1995 • Retired: 1996
Market Value: $150

(107)

Rags™
12" • Bear • #5102
Issued: 1992 • Retired: 1996
Market Value: $70

(108)
New!

Romeo™
14" • Bear • #5310
Issued: 1998 • Current
A. Gold Ribbon/I Love You (1998-Current)
B. Purple Ribbon/Mother's Day (1998)
C. Red Ribbon (1998)
Market Value: A–$_____ B–$37 C–N/E

(109)

Ruffles™
12" • Bear • #5014
Issued: 1995 • Retired: 1995
Market Value: $90

BEARS

	Date Purchased	Price Paid	Value of My Collection
106.			
107.			
108.			
109.			
110.			
✏ PENCIL TOTALS			

(110)

Rufus™
18" • Bear • #5015
Issued: 1993 • Retired: 1997
Market Value: $50

111

Rumples™
18" • Bear • #5002
Issued: 1995 • Retired: 1996
Market Value: $70

112

Rumples™
18" • Bear • #5003
Issued: 1995 • Retired: 1995
A. Brown Nose/Green Ribbon (1995)
B. Pink Nose/Pink Ribbon (1995)
Market Value: A/B–$85

113

Sam™
18" • Bear • #5010
Issued: 1995 • Retired: 1996
Market Value: $225

114

Scruffy™
18" • Bear • #5012
Issued: 1991 • Retired: 1994
Market Value: $150

115

Scruffy™
18" • Bear • #5013
Issued: 1992 • Retired: 1995
A. Gold (1995)
B. Cream (1992)
Market Value: A–N/E B–$200

BEARS

	Date Purchased	Price Paid	Value of My Collection
111.			
112.			
113.			
114.			
115.			
PENCIL TOTALS			

BEARS

131

(116)

Shadow™
20" • Bear • #5011
Issued: 1994 • Retired: 1996
Market Value: $53

(117)

Shaggy™
18" • Bear • #5303
Issued: 1992 • Retired: 1993
A. 18" (1993)
B. 24" (1992)
Market Value: A/B–$180

(118)

Shaggy™
18" • Bear • #5304
Issued: 1992 • Retired: 1994
Market Value: $180

(119)

Shaggy™
18" • Bear • #5305
Issued: 1993 • Retired: 1996
Market Value: $100

BEARS

	Date Purchased	Price Paid	Value of My Collection
116.			
117.			
118.			
119.			
✏ PENCIL TOTALS			

(120)

Snowball™
14" • Bear • #5002
Issued: 1988 • Retired: 1993
A. 14"/Red Ribbon (1991-1993)
B. 13"/Red Ribbon (1990)
C. 13"/Blue Ribbon (1989)
D. 13"/No Ribbon (1988)
Market Value: A/B/C/D–N/E

(121)

Spice™
18" • Bear • #5020
Issued: 1996 • Retired: 1997
Market Value: $50

(122)

Sugar™
14" • Bear • #5007
Issued: 1995 • Retired: 1995
Market Value: $90

(123)

Sugar™
14" • Polar Bear • #5008
Issued: 1990 • Retired: 1991
A. 14" (1991)
B. 20" (1990)
Market Value: A/B–N/E

(124)

Super Buddy™
32" • Bear • #9006
Issued: 1990 • Retired: 1991
Market Value: N/E

BEARS

	Date Purchased	Price Paid	Value of My Collection
120.			
121.			
122.			
123.			
124.			
PENCIL TOTALS			

BEARS

133

(125)

Super McGee™
26" • Bear • #9005
Issued: 1991 • Retired: 1991
Market Value: N/E

(126)

Super Ping Pong™
26" • Panda • #9010
Issued: 1991 • Retired: 1991
Market Value: N/E

(127)

Super PJ™
24" • Bear • #9012
Issued: 1991 • Retired: 1991
Market Value: N/E

(128)

Super Scruffy™
28" • Bear • #9000
Issued: 1991 • Retired: 1991
Market Value: $400

BEARS

	Date Purchased	Price Paid	Value of My Collection
125.			
126.			
127.			
128.			
129.			
✎ PENCIL TOTALS			

(129)

Super Snowball™
26" • Bear • #9009
Issued: 1991 • Retired: 1991
Market Value: N/E

(130)

Theodore™
19" • Bear • #5501
Issued: 1996 • Retired: 1997
Market Value: $60

(131)

Vanilla™
18" • Bear • #5012
Issued: 1996 • Retired: 1997
Market Value: $56

(132)

Wuzzy™
13" • Bear • #5202
Issued: 1996 • Retired: 1997
Market Value: $90

(133)

*photo
not
available*

Yukon™
N/A • Bear • #7424
Issued: 1996 • Retired: 1996
Market Value: $90

	Date Purchased	Price Paid	Value of My Collection
BEARS			
130.			
131.			
132.			
133.			
PENCIL TOTALS			

BEARS

(134)

Al E. Kat™
22" • Cat • #1111
Issued: 1988 • Current
A. 22"/Curled (1996-Current)
B. 20"/Curled (1992-95)
C. 20"/Flat (1989-91)
D. 23"/Flat (1988)
Market Value: A–$_____ B–N/E
C–$80 D–N/E

(135)

Al E. Kat™
22" • Cat • #1112
Issued: 1989 • Current
A. 22"/Curled (1996-Current)
B. 20"/Curled (1992-95)
C. 20"/Flat (1989-91)
Market Value: A–$_____ B–N/E C–$80

(136)

Angel™
20" • Persian • #1001
Issued: 1988 • Retired: 1995
Market Value: $80

(137)

Angel™
20" • Himalayan • #1001H
Issued: 1988 • Retired: 1990
Market Value: N/E

CATS

	Date Purchased	Price Paid	Value of My Collection
134.			
135.			
136.			
137.			
138.			
PENCIL TOTALS			

(138)

New!

Angel™
17" • Persian • #1122
Issued: 1998 • Current
Market Value: $_____

(139)

Angora™
N/A • Cat • #1001
Issued: 1986 • Retired: 1986
Market Value: N/E

(140)

Baby Angora™
N/A • Cat • #1002
Issued: 1986 • Retired: 1986
Market Value: N/E

(141)

Baby Bijan™
N/A • Cat • #1006
Issued: 1986 • Retired: 1986
Market Value: N/E

(142)

Baby Butterball™
N/A • Cat • #2006
Issued: 1986 • Retired: 1986
Market Value: N/E

CATS

	Date Purchased	Price Paid	Value of My Collection
139.			
140.			
141.			
142.			
✏ PENCIL TOTALS			

CATS

(143)

Baby Jasmine™
N/A • Cat • #1004
Issued: 1986 • Retired: 1986
Market Value: N/E

(144)

Baby Kasha™
N/A • Cat • #1008
Issued: 1986 • Retired: 1986
Market Value: N/E

(145)

*photo
not
available*

Baby Kimchi™
N/A • Cat • #2004
Issued: 1986 • Retired: 1986
Market Value: N/E

(146)

Baby Oscar™
N/A • Cat • #2008
Issued: 1986 • Retired: 1986
Market Value: N/E

CATS

	Date Purchased	Price Paid	Value of My Collection
143.			
144.			
145.			
146.			
147.			
✏ PENCIL TOTALS			

(147)

*photo
not
available*

Baby Snowball™
N/A • Cat • #2002
Issued: 1986 • Retired: 1986
Market Value: N/E

(148)

Bijan™
N/A • Cat • #1005
Issued: 1986 • Retired: 1986
Market Value: N/E

(149) New!

Boots™
16" • Cat • #1123
Issued: 1998 • Current
Market Value: $_____

(150)

*photo
not
available*

Butterball™
N/A • Cat • #2005
Issued: 1986 • Retired: 1986
Market Value: N/E

(151)

Coal™
16" • Cat • #1119
Issued: 1997 • Retired: 1997
Market Value: $40

(152)

Crystal™
16" • Cat • #1120
Issued: 1997 • Current
Market Value: $_____

CATS

	Date Purchased	Price Paid	Value of My Collection
148.			
149.			
150.			
151.			
152.			
✏ PENCIL TOTALS			

CATS

139

153

Fluffy™
15" • Persian • #1002
Issued: 1996 • Retired: 1997
Market Value: $40

154

Frisky™
17" • Cat • #1007
Issued: 1996 • Retired: 1997
Market Value: $130

155

Ginger™
20" • Cat • #1007
Issued: 1988 • Retired: 1990
Market Value: $425

156

Ginger™
20" • Himalayan • #1007H
Issued: 1988 • Retired: 1990
Market Value: N/E

Cats

	Date Purchased	Price Paid	Value of My Collection
153.			
154.			
155.			
156.			
✏ PENCIL TOTALS			

(157)

Jasmine™
N/A • Cat • #1003
Issued: 1986 • Retired: 1986
Market Value: N/E

(158)

Kasha™
N/A • Cat • #1007
Issued: 1986 • Retired: 1986
Market Value: N/E

(159)

Kimchi™
N/A • Cat • #2003
Issued: 1986 • Retired: 1986
Market Value: N/E

(160)

Licorice™
20" • Persian • #1009
Issued: 1988 • Retired: 1995
Market Value: $80

(161)
New!

Licorice™
17" • Persian • #1125
Issued: 1998 • Current
Market Value: $____

CATS

	Date Purchased	Price Paid	Value of My Collection
157.			
158.			
159.			
160.			
161.			
✏ PENCIL TOTALS			

CATS

141

(162)

Maggie™
22" • Cat • #1115
Issued: 1992 • Current
A. 22"/Curled (1996-Current)
B. 20"/Flat (1992-95)
Market Value: A–$_____ B–$75

(163)

Mittens™
12" • Cat • #1117
Issued: 1993 • Retired: 1994
Market Value: $225

(164)

Mittens™
12" • Cat • #1118
Issued: 1993 • Retired: 1994
Market Value: $225

(165)

*photo
not
available*

Oscar™
N/A • Cat • #2007
Issued: 1986 • Retired: 1986
Market Value: N/E

Cats

	Date Purchased	Price Paid	Value of My Collection
162.			
163.			
164.			
165.			
166.			
✏ PENCIL TOTALS			

(166)

Patches™
20" • Cat • #1114
Issued: 1991 • Retired: 1995
Market Value: $140

(167)

Peaches™
20" • Cat • #1003
Issued: 1988 • Retired: 1993
Market Value: $400

(168)

Peaches™
20" • Himalayan • #1003H
Issued: 1988 • Retired: 1990
Market Value: N/E

(169)

Puffy™
15" • Persian • #1003
Issued: 1996 • Retired: 1997
Market Value: $40

(170)

Scratch™
15" • Cat • #1117
Issued: 1996 • Retired: 1997
Market Value: $85

(171)

Screech™
15" • Cat • #1116
Issued: 1995 • Retired: 1996
A. Collar (1996)
B. No Collar (1995)
Market Value: A/B–$100

CATS

	Date Purchased	Price Paid	Value of My Collection
167.			
168.			
169.			
170.			
171.			
✏ PENCIL TOTALS			

CATS

(172)

Shadow™
20" • Cat • #1112
Issued: 1988 • Retired: 1988
Market Value: N/E

(173)

Sherlock™
20" • Cat • #1110
Issued: 1990 • Retired: 1992
Market Value: $450

(174)

Silky™
15" • Persian • #1004
Issued: 1996 • Retired: 1997
Market Value: $40

(175)

Smokey™
20" • Cat • #1005
Issued: 1988 • Retired: 1993
Market Value: $300

CATS

	Date Purchased	Price Paid	Value of My Collection
172.			
173.			
174.			
175.			
176.			
✏ PENCIL TOTALS			

(176)

Smokey™
20" • Himalayan • #1005H
Issued: 1988 • Retired: 1990
Market Value: N/E

photo
not
available

Snowball™
N/A • Cat • #2001
Issued: 1986 • Retired: 1986
Market Value: N/E

Socks™
12" • Cat • #1116
Issued: 1993 • Retired: 1994
Market Value: $220

New!

Spice™
17" • Cat • #1121
Issued: 1998 • Current
Market Value: $_____

Tumbles™
17" • Cat • #1008
Issued: 1996 • Retired: 1997
Market Value: $100

CATS

	Date Purchased	Price Paid	Value of My Collection
177.			
178.			
179.			
180.			
PENCIL TOTALS			

CATS

(181)
New!

Ace™
12" • Dalmatian • #2027
Issued: 1998 • Current
Market Value: $_____

(182)

Ashes™
8" • Labrador Retriever • #2018
Issued: 1996 • Retired: 1996
Market Value: $50

(183)

Baby Schnapps™
N/A • Dog • #3001
Issued: 1986 • Retired: 1986
Market Value: N/E

(184)

Baby Sparky™
20" • Dalmatian • #2012
Issued: 1992 • Retired: 1994
A. Tongue (1994)
B. No Tongue (1992-93)
Market Value: A/B–$150

DOGS

	Date Purchased	Price Paid	Value of My Collection
181.			
182.			
183.			
184.			
185.			
✏ PENCIL TOTALS			

(185)

Barney™
20" • Labrador Retriever • #2003
Issued: 1990 • Retired: 1992
Market Value: $725

(186)

Biscuit™
17" • Dog • #2026
Issued: 1997 • Retired: 1997
Market Value: $40

(187)

Bo™
20" • Basset Hound • #2009
Issued: 1994 • Retired: 1995
Market Value: $275

(188)

Buckshot™
20" • Basset Hound • #2009
Issued: 1992 • Retired: 1993
Market Value: $520

(189)

Buster™
20" • Cocker Spaniel • #2005
Issued: 1990 • Retired: 1991
Market Value: $600

(190)

Charlie™
20" • Cocker Spaniel • #2001
Issued: 1988 • Retired: 1990
A. Tongue (1990)
B. No Tongue (1988-89)
Market Value: A/B–N/E

DOGS

	Date Purchased	Price Paid	Value of My Collection
186.			
187.			
188.			
189.			
190.			
✎ PENCIL TOTALS			

DOGS

(191)

Charlie™
20" • Cocker Spaniel • #2005
Issued: 1994 • Retired: 1997
A. Floppy (1996-97)
B. Sitting (1994-95)
Market Value: A–$42 B–$68

(192)

Chips™
12" • Dog • #2025
Issued: 1997 • Current
Market Value: $_____

(193)

Churchill™
12" • Bulldog • #2017
Issued: 1996 • Current
Market Value: $_____

(194)

Cinders™
20" • Labrador Retriever • #2008
Issued: 1994 • Retired: 1997
A. Sitting/Black & Brown (1995-97)
B. Floppy/All Black (1994)
Market Value: A/B–$65

DOGS

	Date Purchased	Price Paid	Value of My Collection
191.			
192.			
193.			
194.			
195.			
✏ PENCIL TOTALS			

(195)

Corky™
12" • Cocker Spaniel • #2023
Issued: 1996 • Current
Market Value: $_____

(196)

Dopey™
17" • Dog • #2022
Issued: 1996 • Retired: 1997
Market Value: $115

(197)

Droopy™
15" • Hound • #2009
Issued: 1996 • Retired: 1997
Market Value: $54

(198)

Elvis™
20" • Hound • #2010
Issued: 1995 • Current
Market Value: $_____

(199)

Fido™
8" • Dog • #2019
Issued: 1996 • Retired: 1996
Market Value: $52

(200)

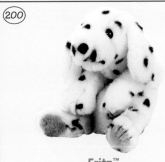

Fritz™
20" • Dalmatian • #2002
Issued: 1988 • Retired: 1990
A. Tongue (1990)
B. No Tongue (1988-89)
Market Value: A/B–$380

DOGS

	Date Purchased	Price Paid	Value of My Collection
196.			
197.			
198.			
199.			
200.			
PENCIL TOTALS			

Dogs

201

Honey™
20" • Dog • #2001
Issued: 1995 • Current
Market Value: $_____

202

*photo
not
available*

Large Max™
N/A • Dog • #9001
Issued: 1992 • Retired: 1992
Market Value: N/E

203

Large Rusty™
26" • Mutt • #9011
Issued: 1994 • Retired: 1995
Market Value: $140

204

Large Scruffy™
26" • Dog • #9011
Issued: 1992 • Retired: 1993
Market Value: $225

Dogs

	Date Purchased	Price Paid	Value of My Collection
201.			
202.			
203.			
204.			
205.			
PENCIL TOTALS			

205

Large Sparky™
26" • Dalmatian • #9002
Issued: 1992 • Retired: 1993
Market Value: $255

206

Max™
20" • Dog • #2008
Issued: 1991 • Retired: 1992
Market Value: $315

207

Max™
20" • Dog • #3001
Issued: 1988 • Retired: 1990
A. Tongue (1990)
B. No Tongue (1988-89)
Market Value: A/B–$900

208

Muffin™
13" • Dog • #2020
Issued: 1996 • Current
Market Value: $_____

209

Patches™
18" • Dog • #2003
Issued: 1996 • Current
Market Value: $_____

210

Pepper™
12" • Labrador Retriever • #2024
Issued: 1997 • Current
Market Value: $_____

Dogs

	Date Purchased	Price Paid	Value of My Collection
206.			
207.			
208.			
209.			
210.			
✎ PENCIL TOTALS			

Dogs

(211)

Pierre™
10" • Poodle • #2004
Issued: 1995 • Retired: 1996
Market Value: $60

(212)

Rusty™
20" • Mutt • #2011
Issued: 1992 • Retired: 1996
Market Value: $48

(213)

Sarge™
20" • German Shepherd • #2003
Issued: 1994 • Retired: 1995
Market Value: $350

(214)

Schnapps™
N/A • Dog • #3000
Issued: 1986 • Retired: 1986
Market Value: N/E

Dogs

	Date Purchased	Price Paid	Value of My Collection
211.			
212.			
213.			
214.			
215.			
PENCIL TOTALS			

(215)

Scruffy™
20" • Dog • #2000
Issued: 1992 • Retired: 1996
A. Red Ribbon/White (1993-1996)
B. Blue Ribbon/Cream (1992)
Market Value: A–$80 B–$190

(216)

Scruffy™
20" • Dog • #2001
Issued: 1991 • Retired: 1994
A. Ribbon (1992-94)
B. No Ribbon (1991)
Market Value: A/B–$155

(217)
New!

Sherlock™
12" • Basset Hound • #2029
Issued: 1998 • Current
Market Value: $_____

(218)

Sniffles™
18" • Dog • #2021
Issued: 1996 • Retired: 1996
Market Value: $150

(219)

Spanky™
20" • St. Bernard • #2010
Issued: 1992 • Retired: 1993
Market Value: N/E

(220)

Spanky™
8" • Cocker Spaniel • #2015
Issued: 1996 • Retired: 1996
Market Value: $55

DOGS

	Date Purchased	Price Paid	Value of My Collection
216.			
217.			
218.			
219.			
220.			
PENCIL TOTALS			

DOGS

153

(221)

Sparky™
20" • Dalmatian • #2004
Issued: 1990 • Retired: 1993
Market Value: $200

(222)

Sparky™
20" • Dalmatian • #2012
Issued: 1995 • Retired: 1995
Market Value: $150

(223)

New!

Sunny™
14" • Dog • #2028
Issued: 1998 • Current
Market Value: $_____

(224)

Super Fritz™
36" • Dalmatian • #9002
Issued: 1989 • Retired: 1989
Market Value: N/E

DOGS

	Date Purchased	Price Paid	Value of My Collection
221.			
222.			
223.			
224.			
225.			

✏ PENCIL TOTALS

(225)

Super Max™
32" • Dog • #3002
Issued: 1988 • Retired: 1990
A. Tongue (1990)
B. No Tongue (1988-89)
Market Value: A/B–$700

(226)

Super Max™
26" • Dog • #9001
Issued: 1991 • Retired: 1992
A. 26" (1992)
B. 32" (1991)
Market Value: A/B–$560

(227)

Super Schnapps™
N/A • Dog • #3002
Issued: 1986 • Retired: 1986
Market Value: N/E

(228)

Super Scruffy™
32" • Dog • #9011
Issued: 1991 • Retired: 1991
Market Value: N/E

(229)

Super Sparky™
32" • Dalmatian • #9002
Issued: 1990 • Retired: 1991
Market Value: $500

(230)

Taffy™
12" • Terrier • #2014
Issued: 1996 • Current
A. 12" (1998-Current)
B. 8" (1996-97)
Market Value: A–$_____ B–$25

DOGS

	Date Purchased	Price Paid	Value of My Collection
226.			
227.			
228.			
229.			
230.			
✏ PENCIL TOTALS			

DOGS

(231)

Timber™
20" • Husky • #2002
Issued: 1994 • Current
Market Value: $_____

(232)

Toffee™
20" • Terrier • #2013
Issued: 1993 • Retired: 1998
Market Value: $35

(233)

Winston™
20" • Bulldog • #2007
Issued: 1991 • Current
Market Value: $_____

(234)

Yappy™
12" • Yorkshire Terrier • #2016
Issued: 1996 • Current
A. 12" (1998-Current)
B. 8" (1996-97)
Market Value: A–$_____ B–$35

Dogs

	Date Purchased	Price Paid	Value of My Collection
231.			
232.			
233.			
234.			
235.			
✏ PENCIL TOTALS			

(235)

Yorkie™
20" • Yorkshire Terrier • #2006
Issued: 1991 • Retired: 1996
Market Value: $80

(236)

Angora™
14" • Rabbit • #8004
Issued: 1995 • Retired: 1995
Market Value: $80

(237)

Angora™
20" • Rabbit • #8005
Issued: 1991 • Retired: 1992
Market Value: $380

(238)

*photo
not
available*

Arnold™
20" • Pig • #6001
Issued: 1988 • Retired: 1989
Market Value: N/E

(239)

Arnold™
20" • Pig • #6002
Issued: 1990 • Retired: 1990
Market Value: $325

(240)

Baby Clover™
12" • Cow • #8023
Issued: 1993 • Retired: 1994
Market Value: $105

COUNTRY

	Date Purchased	Price Paid	Value of My Collection
236.			
237.			
238.			
239.			
240.			
PENCIL TOTALS			

COUNTRY

(241)

Baby Curly Bunny™
12" • Bunny • #8024
Issued: 1993 • Retired: 1997
Market Value: $42

(242)

Baby Curly Bunny™
12" • Bunny • #8025
Issued: 1993 • Retired: 1997
Market Value: $35

(243)

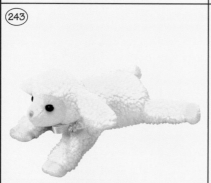

Baby Lovie™
20" • Lamb • #8019
Issued: 1992 • Retired: 1992
Market Value: N/E

(244)

Baby Lovie™
12" • Lamb • #8020
Issued: 1993 • Retired: 1994
Market Value: $100

Country

	Date Purchased	Price Paid	Value of My Collection
241.			
242.			
243.			
244.			
245.			
PENCIL TOTALS			

(245)

Baby Petunia™
12" • Pig • #8021
Issued: 1993 • Retired: 1994
A. Red Ribbon (1994)
B. Blue Ribbon (1993)
Market Value: A/B–$120

(246)

Baby Pokey™
13" • Rabbit • #8022
Issued: 1996 • Retired: 1997
Market Value: $33

(247)

Baby Smokey™
13" • Rabbit • #8023
Issued: 1996 • Retired: 1997
Market Value: $30

(248)

Bandit™
20" • Raccoon • #1119
Issued: 1990 • Retired: 1990
Market Value: $600

(249)

Beanie Bunny™
12" • Bunny • #8000
Issued: 1989 • Retired: 1992
Market Value: $750

(250)

Beanie Bunny™
12" • Bunny • #8001
Issued: 1991 • Retired: 1992
Market Value: $750

COUNTRY

	Date Purchased	Price Paid	Value of My Collection
246.			
247.			
248.			
249.			
250.			
PENCIL TOTALS			

COUNTRY

(251)

Big Beanie Bunny™
15" • Bunny • #8011
Issued: 1990 • Retired: 1992
A. Gold Ribbon (1991-92)
B. Pink Ribbon (1990)
Market Value: A/B–**$750**

(252)

Big Beanie Bunny™
15" • Bunny • #8012
Issued: 1991 • Retired: 1992
Market Value: $750

(253)

Blossom™
18" • Rabbit • #8013
Issued: 1996 • Retired: 1997
Market Value: $120

(254)

New!

Bows™
11" • Rabbit • #8030
Issued: 1998 • Current
Market Value: $_____

COUNTRY			
	Date Purchased	Price Paid	Value of My Collection
251.			
252.			
253.			
254.			
255.			
✏ PENCIL TOTALS			

(255)

Buttercup™
18" • Rabbit • #8012
Issued: 1996 • Retired: 1997
Market Value: $165

256 New!

Buttons™
11" • Rabbit • #8031
Issued: 1998 • Current
Market Value: $_____

257

Candy™
N/A • Rabbit • #8011
Issued: 1996 • Retired: 1996
Market Value: $60

258

Chestnut™
12" • Squirrel • #8022
Issued: 1993 • Retired: 1993
Market Value: $130

259

Clover™
20" • Cow • #8007
Issued: 1991 • Retired: 1996
A. Ribbon (1996)
B. No Ribbon (1994-95)
C. Ribbon (1991-93)
Market Value: A/B/C–$80

260

Cotton™
14" • Rabbit • #8003
Issued: 1996 • Retired: 1997
Market Value: $50

COUNTRY

	Date Purchased	Price Paid	Value of My Collection
256.			
257.			
258.			
259.			
260.			
PENCIL TOTALS			

COUNTRY

(261)

Curly Bunny™
22" • Bunny • #8017
Issued: 1992 • Current
Market Value: $_____

(262)

Curly Bunny™
22" • Bunny • #8018
Issued: 1992 • Current
Market Value: $_____

(263)

Domino™
20" • Rabbit • #8006
Issued: 1991 • Retired: 1992
Market Value: $430

(264)

Freddie™
12" • Frog • #1117
Issued: 1989 • Retired: 1990
A. 12" (1990)
B. 10" (1989)
Market Value: A/B–N/E

Country

	Date Purchased	Price Paid	Value of My Collection
261.			
262.			
263.			
264.			
265.			
✏ PENCIL TOTALS			

(265)

photo
not
available

Freddie™
N/A • Frog • #8002
Issued: 1989 • Retired: 1989
Market Value: N/E

(266)

Hooters™
9" • Owl • #8016
Issued: 1992 • Retired: 1994
Market Value: $400

(267)

Jersey™
20" • Cow • #8026
Issued: 1997 • Current
A. Black & White (1997-Current)
B. Brown & White (1997)
Market Value: A–$_____ B–$40

(268)

Large Curly Bunny™
24" • Bunny • #9003
Issued: 1994 • Retired: 1997
Market Value: $76

(269)

Large Curly Bunny™
24" • Bunny • #9007
Issued: 1996 • Retired: 1997
Market Value: $76

(270)

Large Petunia™
26" • Pig • #9003
Issued: 1992 • Retired: 1992
Market Value: $450

COUNTRY

	Date Purchased	Price Paid	Value of My Collection
266.			
267.			
268.			
269.			
270.			
✏ PENCIL TOTALS			

COUNTRY

(271)

Lillie™
20" • Lamb • #8004
Issued: 1990 • Retired: 1990
Market Value: $550

(272)

Lovie™
18" • Lamb • #8001
Issued: 1988 • Retired: 1990
Market Value: $670

(273)

Lovie™
20" • Lamb • #8004
Issued: 1991 • Retired: 1993
Market Value: $300

(274)

Lovie™
20" • Lamb • #8019
Issued: 1993 • Retired: 1996
Market Value: $85

COUNTRY

	Date Purchased	Price Paid	Value of My Collection
271.			
272.			
273.			
274.			
275.			
✏ PENCIL TOTALS			

(275) *New!*

Lovie™
10" • Lamb • #8027
Issued: 1998 • Retired: 1998
Market Value: $30

(276)

Nibbles™
9" • Bunny • #8000
Issued: 1994 • Current
Market Value: $_____

(277)

Nibbles™
9" • Bunny • #8001
Issued: 1995 • Current
Market Value: $_____

(278)

Peepers™
9" • Chick • #8015
Issued: 1991 • Retired: 1994
A. Feet (1992-94)
B. No Feet (1991)
Market Value: A/B–$165

(279)

Peter™
14" • Rabbit • #8002
Issued: 1989 • Retired: 1997
A. 14"/Jointed (1996-97)
B. 20"/Not Jointed (1989-94)
Market Value: A–$40 B–$300

(280)

Petunia™
20" • Pig • #6001
Issued: 1989 • Retired: 1990
Market Value: N/E

COUNTRY

	Date Purchased	Price Paid	Value of My Collection
276.			
277.			
278.			
279.			
280.			
✏ PENCIL TOTALS			

COUNTRY

Petunia™
20" • Pig • #8008
Issued: 1991 • Retired: 1995
A. Red Ribbon (1994-95)
B. Blue Ribbon (1993)
C. Pink Ribbon (1991-92)
Market Value: A–$110 B–$140 C–$170

Pokey™
19" • Rabbit • #8015
Issued: 1996 • Retired: 1997
Market Value: $62

Rosie™
20" • Rabbit • #8003
Issued: 1990 • Retired: 1994
Market Value: $370

Smokey™
19" • Rabbit • #8016
Issued: 1996 • Retired: 1997
Market Value: $50

COUNTRY

	Date Purchased	Price Paid	Value of My Collection
281.			
282.			
283.			
284.			
285.			
✏ PENCIL TOTALS			

Sparkles™
20" • Unicorn • #8100
Issued: 1997 • Current
Market Value: $_____

(286)

Super Arnold™
32" • Pig • #9003
Issued: 1990 • Retired: 1990
Market Value: N/E

(287)

Super Petunia™
32" • Pig • #9003
Issued: 1989 • Retired: 1991
A. 32"/Ribbon (1991)
B. 36"/No Ribbon (1989)
Market Value: A/B–N/E

(288)

Tulip™
18" • Pig • #8008
Issued: 1996 • Current
Market Value: $_____

(289)

Whinnie™
20" • Horse • #8006
Issued: 1994 • Retired: 1995
Market Value: $260

(290)

Woolly™
9" • Lamb • #8005
Issued: 1996 • Current
Market Value: $_____

COUNTRY

	Date Purchased	Price Paid	Value of My Collection
286.			
287.			
288.			
289.			
290.			
PENCIL TOTALS			

COUNTRY

(291)

Arctic™
12" • Polar Bear • #7419
Issued: 1995 • Retired: 1997
Market Value: $55

(292)

Baby George™
12" • Gorilla • #7300
Issued: 1996 • Current
Market Value: $_____

(293)

Bandit™
20" • Raccoon • #8009
Issued: 1991 • Retired: 1996
A. Brown (1992-96)
B. Gray (1991)
Market Value: A–$65 B–N/E

(294)

Bengal™
12" • Tiger • #7423
Issued: 1995 • Current
A. Floppy/Gold Chest (1998-Current)
B. Sitting/White Chest (1995-97)
Market Value: A–$_____ B–$30

Wildlife

	Date Purchased	Price Paid	Value of My Collection
291.			
292.			
293.			
294.			
✏ PENCIL TOTALS			

(295)

Big George™
27" • Gorilla • #7302
Issued: 1990 • Current
Market Value: $_____

(296)

Big Jake™
16" • Monkey • #7002
Issued: 1989 • Retired: 1989
Market Value: $400

(297)

Big Jake™
16" • Monkey • #7002A
Issued: 1989 • Retired: 1989
Market Value: $425

(298)

Big Jake™
16" • Monkey • #7002C
Issued: 1989 • Retired: 1989
Market Value: $425

(299)

Big Jake™
16" • Monkey • #7200
Issued: 1990 • Retired: 1990
Market Value: N/E

WILDLIFE

	Date Purchased	Price Paid	Value of My Collection
295.			
296.			
297.			
298.			
299.			
✏ PENCIL TOTALS			

WILDLIFE

(300)

Big Jake™
16" • Monkey • #7201
Issued: 1990 • Retired: 1990
Market Value: $400

(301)

Big Jake™
16" • Monkey • #7202
Issued: 1990 • Retired: 1990
Market Value: N/E

(302) New!

Cha Cha™
12" • Monkey • #7005
Issued: 1998 • Current
Market Value: $_____

(303)

Chi-Chi™
20" • Cheetah • #1114
Issued: 1989 • Retired: 1990
A. No Ribbon (1990)
B. Ribbon (1989)
Market Value: A/B–$880

(304)

Chi-Chi™
20" • Cheetah • #7414
Issued: 1991 • Retired: 1992
Market Value: $620

WILDLIFE

	Date Purchased	Price Paid	Value of My Collection
300.			
301.			
302.			
303.			
304.			
PENCIL TOTALS			

(305)

Chuckles™
15" • Chimp • #7303
Issued: 1997 • Retired: 1997
Market Value: $50

(306)

Dakota™
12" • Wolf • #7418
Issued: 1995 • Current
A. 12"/Floppy (1998-Current)
B. 8"/Sitting (1997)
C. 12"/Sitting (1995-97)
Market Value: A–$_____ B–N/E C–$40

(307)

Elmer™
20" • Elephant • #1116
Issued: 1989 • Retired: 1990
A. No Ribbon (1990)
B. Ribbon (1989)
Market Value: A/B–N/E

(308)

Elmer™
20" • Elephant • #7416
Issued: 1991 • Retired: 1996
A. Gray Ears/Long Trunk (1994-96)
B. White Ears/Short Trunk (1991-93)
Market Value: A–$115 B–$305

(309)

Freddie™
16" • Frog • #8010
Issued: 1991 • Current
A. 16" (1995-Current)
B. 12" (1991)
Market Value: A–$_____ B–N/E

WILDLIFE

	Date Purchased	Price Paid	Value of My Collection
305.			
306.			
307.			
308.			
309.			
PENCIL TOTALS			

WILDLIFE

③⑩

George™
20" • Gorilla • #7301
Issued: 1990 • Current
Market Value: $_____

③①

Harris™
20" • Lion • #1115
Issued: 1989 • Retired: 1990
A. Gold & Tan Mane (1990)
B. Gold Mane (1989)
Market Value: A/B–N/E

③⑫

Harris™
20" • Lion • #7415
Issued: 1991 • Retired: 1996
Market Value: $80

③⑬

Jake™
12" • Monkey • #7001
Issued: 1988 • Retired: 1989
Market Value: $750

WILDLIFE

	Date Purchased	Price Paid	Value of My Collection
310.			
311.			
312.			
313.			
314.			
✎ PENCIL TOTALS			

③⑭

Jake™
12" • Monkey • #7001A
Issued: 1989 • Retired: 1989
Market Value: $750

(315)

Jake™
N/A • Monkey • #7001B
Issued: 1989 • Retired: 1989
Market Value: N/E

(316)

Jake™
12" • Monkey • #7001C
Issued: 1989 • Retired: 1989
Market Value: $750

(317)

Jake™
N/A • Monkey • #7001R
Issued: 1989 • Retired: 1989
Market Value: N/E

(318)

Jake™
24" • Monkey • #7100
Issued: 1990 • Retired: 1994
A. 24" (1992-94)
B. 22" (1991)
C. 12" (1990)
Market Value: A–$330 B–$330 C–N/E

(319)

Jake™
24" • Monkey • #7101
Issued: 1990 • Retired: 1993
A. 24" (1992-93)
B. 22" (1991)
C. 12" (1990)
Market Value: A–$300 B–$300 C–N/E

WILDLIFE

	Date Purchased	Price Paid	Value of My Collection
315.			
316.			
317.			
318.			
319.			
✎ PENCIL TOTALS			

WILDLIFE

(320)

Jake™
12" • Monkey • #7102
Issued: 1990 • Retired: 1990
Market Value: N/E

(321)

Josh™
24" • Monkey • #7101
Issued: 1994 • Retired: 1996
Market Value: $90

(322)

Jumbo George™
48" • Gorilla • #9008
Issued: 1991 • Current
Market Value: $____

(323)

Leo™
22" • Lion • #7427
Issued: 1997 • Current
Market Value: $____

WILDLIFE

	Date Purchased	Price Paid	Value of My Collection
320.			
321.			
322.			
323.			
324.			
✏ PENCIL TOTALS			

(324)

Mango™
20" • Monkey • #7100
Issued: 1995 • Current
Market Value: $____

(325)

Mango™
20" • Monkey • #7102
Issued: 1995 • Current
Market Value: $_____

(326)

Mischief™
18" • Monkey • #7000
Issued: 1988 • Retired: 1993
A. White (1991-93)
B. Auburn (1990)
C. White (1988-89)
Market Value: A–$350 B–N/E C–$350

(327)

Mischief™
18" • Monkey • #7000A
Issued: 1989 • Retired: 1989
Market Value: N/E

(328)

Mischief™
N/A • Monkey • #7000B
Issued: 1989 • Retired: 1989
Market Value: N/E

(329)

Mischief™
18" • Monkey • #7000C
Issued: 1989 • Retired: 1989
Market Value: N/E

WILDLIFE

	Date Purchased	Price Paid	Value of My Collection
325.			
326.			
327.			
328.			
329.			
✏ PENCIL TOTALS			

WILDLIFE

(330)

Mischief™
N/A • Monkey • #7000R
Issued: 1989 • Retired: 1989
Market Value: N/E

(331)

Mischief™
18" • Monkey • #7001
Issued: 1990 • Retired: 1993
A. Auburn (1991-93)
B. White (1990)
Market Value: A–$320 B–N/E

(332)

Mischief™
18" • Monkey • #7002
Issued: 1990 • Retired: 1991
Market Value: N/E

(333)

Mischief™
21" • Monkey • #7414
Issued: 1996 • Retired: 1997
Market Value: $120

WILDLIFE

	Date Purchased	Price Paid	Value of My Collection
330.			
331.			
332.			
333.			
✎ PENCIL TOTALS			

(334)

Misty™
14" • Seal • #7400
Issued: 1991 • Retired: 1994
A. 14"/Ribbon (1993-94)
B. 12"/No Ribbon (1991-92)
Market Value: A/B–$150

(335) New!

Misty™
11" • Seal • #7431
Issued: 1998 • Current
Market Value: $_____

(336)

Mortimer™
18" • Moose • #7417
Issued: 1996 • Current
Market Value: $_____

(337)

Otto™
20" • Otter • #7417
Issued: 1993 • Retired: 1994
Market Value: $240

(338)

Patti™
20" • Panther • #1118
Issued: 1989 • Retired: 1990
A. No Ribbon (1990)
B. Ribbon (1989)
Market Value: A/B–$700

WILDLIFE

	Date Purchased	Price Paid	Value of My Collection
334.			
335.			
336.			
337.			
338.			
✏ PENCIL TOTALS			

WILDLIFE

(339)

Rascal™
16" • Monkey • #7001
Issued: 1994 • Retired: 1997
Market Value: $45

(340)

Sahara™
12" • Lion • #7421
Issued: 1995 • Current
A. Floppy/Gold Chest/Long Mane
(1998-Current)
B. Sitting/Gold Chest/Long Mane (1996)
C. Sitting/White Chest/Short Mane (1995)
Market Value: A–$_____ B–$35 C–$35

(341)

Shivers™
9" • Penguin • #7419
Issued: 1993 • Retired: 1994
Market Value: $330

(342)

Spout™
9" • Elephant • #7426
Issued: 1996 • Current
A. Floppy (1998-Current)
B. Sitting (1996-97)
Market Value: A–$_____ B–$28

WILDLIFE

	Date Purchased	Price Paid	Value of My Collection
339.			
340.			
341.			
342.			
343.			
✏ PENCIL TOTALS			

(343)

Super Chi-Chi™
52" • Cheetah • #9004
Issued: 1989 • Retired: 1989
Market Value: N/E

(344)

Super George™
38" • Gorilla • #9007
Issued: 1990 • Retired: 1991
Market Value: $460

(345)

Super Jake™
16" • Monkey • #7002
Issued: 1988 • Retired: 1989
Market Value: N/E

(346)

Super Jake™
N/A • Monkey • #7002B
Issued: 1989 • Retired: 1989
Market Value: N/E

(347)

Super Jake™
N/A • Monkey • #7002R
Issued: 1989 • Retired: 1989
Market Value: N/E

(348)

Super Jake™
55" • Monkey • #9001
Issued: 1989 • Retired: 1989
Market Value: N/E

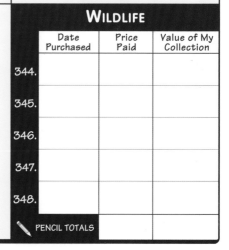

WILDLIFE

	Date Purchased	Price Paid	Value of My Collection
344.			
345.			
346.			
347.			
348.			
PENCIL TOTALS			

WILDLIFE

(349)

Super Tygger™
32" • Tiger • #9004
Issued: 1990 • Retired: 1991
Market Value: N/E

(350)

Tango™
12" • Monkey • #7000
Issued: 1995 • Current
Market Value: $_____

(351)

Tango™
12" • Monkey • #7002
Issued: 1995 • Current
Market Value: $_____

(352)

Twiggy™
23" • Giraffe • #7422
Issued: 1991 • Retired: 1996
Market Value: $130

WILDLIFE			
	Date Purchased	Price Paid	Value of My Collection
349.			
350.			
351.			
352.			
353.			
✏ PENCIL TOTALS			

(353)

Tygger™
20" • Tiger • #1120
Issued: 1990 • Retired: 1990
Market Value: N/E

(354)

Tygger™
20" • Tiger • #7420
Issued: 1991 • Current
A. Floppy (1994-Current)
B. Standing (1992-93)
C. Floppy (1991)
Market Value: A–$_____ B–$255 C–N/E

(355)

Tygger™
20" • Tiger • #7421
Issued: 1991 • Retired: 1992
Market Value: $400

(356)

Wally™
12" • Walrus • #7423
Issued: 1992 • Retired: 1993
Market Value: $160

(357)

Zulu™
20" • Zebra • #7421
Issued: 1994 • Retired: 1994
Market Value: $420

WILDLIFE

	Date Purchased	Price Paid	Value of My Collection
354.			
355.			
356.			
357.			
✏ PENCIL TOTALS			

WILDLIFE

TOTAL VALUE OF MY COLLECTION

Record the value of your collection here by adding the
pencil totals from the bottom of each Value Guide page.

TY® PLUSH ANIMALS

Page Number	Price Paid	Market Value
Page 43		
Page 44		
Page 45		
Page 46		
Page 47		
Page 48		
Page 49		
Page 50		
Page 51		
Page 52		
Page 53		
Page 54		
Page 55		
Page 56		
Page 57		
Page 58		
Page 59		
Page 60		
Page 61		
Page 62		
Page 63		
Page 64		
Page 65		
Page 66		
TOTAL		

TY® PLUSH ANIMALS

Page Number	Price Paid	Market Value
Page 67		
Page 68		
Page 69		
Page 70		
Page 71		
Page 72		
Page 73		
Page 74		
Page 75		
Page 76		
Page 77		
Page 78		
Page 79		
Page 80		
Page 81		
Page 82		
Page 83		
Page 84		
Page 85		
Page 86		
Page 87		
Page 88		
Page 89		
Page 90		
TOTAL		

PAGE SUBTOTALS

PRICE PAID	MARKET VALUE

Record the value of your collection here by adding the
pencil totals from the bottom of each Value Guide page.

Ty® Plush Animals

Page Number	Price Paid	Market Value
Page 91		
Page 92		
Page 93		
Page 94		
Page 95		
Page 96		
Page 97		
Page 98		
Page 99		
Page 100		
Page 101		
Page 102		
Page 103		
Page 104		
Page 105		
Page 106		
Page 107		
Page 108		
Page 109		
Page 110		
Page 111		
Page 112		
Page 113		
TOTAL		

Ty® Plush Animals

Page Number	Price Paid	Market Value
Page 114		
Page 115		
Page 116		
Page 117		
Page 118		
Page 119		
Page 120		
Page 121		
Page 122		
Page 123		
Page 124		
Page 125		
Page 126		
Page 127		
Page 128		
Page 129		
Page 130		
Page 131		
Page 132		
Page 133		
Page 134		
Page 135		
Page 136		
TOTAL		

Page Subtotals

Price Paid	Market Value

TOTAL VALUE OF MY COLLECTION

Record the value of your collection here by adding the
pencil totals from the bottom of each Value Guide page.

TY® PLUSH ANIMALS		
Page Number	Price Paid	Market Value
Page 137		
Page 138		
Page 139		
Page 140		
Page 141		
Page 142		
Page 143		
Page 144		
Page 145		
Page 146		
Page 147		
Page 148		
Page 149		
Page 150		
Page 151		
Page 152		
Page 153		
Page 154		
Page 155		
Page 156		
Page 157		
Page 158		
Page 159		
TOTAL		

TY® PLUSH ANIMALS		
Page Number	Price Paid	Market Value
Page 160		
Page 161		
Page 162		
Page 163		
Page 164		
Page 165		
Page 166		
Page 167		
Page 168		
Page 169		
Page 170		
Page 171		
Page 172		
Page 173		
Page 174		
Page 175		
Page 176		
Page 177		
Page 178		
Page 179		
Page 180		
Page 181		
TOTAL		

GRAND TOTAL		
	PRICE PAID	MARKET VALUE

$\mathcal{N}$o matter which line of Ty plush animals you collect, the secondary market is the place to be. Since Ty Inc. released their first floppy, furry friends in 1986, many changes have taken place to the line itself, as well as to the collectibles industry. When the first of Ty's animals began appearing in stores, they were simply lovable animals that inspired young and old alike to smile. In recent years, however, Ty has transformed itself from a manufacturer of plush children's toys into the hottest prospect on the collectibles market. Therefore, it takes more than hope to complete your collection. In order to do so, you must not only be a savvy shopper, but you must also become well-versed in the secondary market.

THE WILD KINGDOM

The secondary market for collectibles such as Ty plush animals functions on basic supply and demand economics. In many cases, the huge demand for Ty's plush animals has easily outstripped the quantities produced by Ty. Collectors who have difficulty finding pieces to add to their collection are often willing to pay higher prices for "rare" finds.

The incredible interest in the secondary market values of Ty plush animals began with *Beanie Babies*. Fueled by the Internet, word-of-mouth and the *Teenie Beanie Babies* promotion, seemingly thousands of collectors joined the *Beanie Babies* craze daily. As people became more informed by sharing information on the web, an elite group of *Beanie Babies* that had come and gone before the craze hit a fever pitch became highly sought-after.

BEANIE BABIES®
SECONDARY MARKET TIP

Patience Is A Virtue. Like with almost anything, shortage creates demand and, especially with *Beanie Babies*, if shipments are slow to arrive in retail stores, some avid collectors are willing to pay inflated prices on the secondary market just to insure that a particular animal isn't "the one that got away." However, it is likely that these pieces will eventually appear in stores at a much lower retail price.

Beanie Babies collectors first became aware of traditional collectible terms such as **retirements** and **variations**. Those who wanted complete collections realized they had to seek out "retired" pieces which were taken out of production to make room for new designs. Among the coveted designs which retired too early for many collectors were the different color versions of "Teddy" and the dinosaur trio of "Bronty," "Rex" and "Steg." When collectors began to notice that some of their *Beanie Babies* "looked funny," they began to identify variations like the spotless "Spot," wingless "Quacker" and dark blue "Peanut." Once a design changes, the original design is considered "out of production" and that early version often becomes a highly sought-after commodity.

> " . . . many people are speculating that *Attic Treasures* will become the 'next big thing.'"

As the secondary market for *Beanie Babies* became more sophisticated, the Ty **swing tags** and **tush tags** became an important factor. Ty tags have undergone many transformations through the years. The chronology of different tag versions (referred to as "generations" by many collectors) provides a way to determine the approximate age of the plush animal. In the world of *Beanie Babies*, early generation tags are considered by many collectors to be valuable, even for designs that are currently available in stores. And the cardinal rule for *Beanie Babies* collectors is that the tags must stay attached and in perfect condition to maintain full secondary market value.

The popularity of *Beanie Babies* and the strength of the secondary market activity is perhaps unmatched by any collectible in history. Many collectors who enjoy the hunt for rare pieces have turned their attention to *Attic Treasures* or other Ty plush animals. With a slew of recent retirements and a limited supply in stores, many people are speculating that *Attic Treasures* will become the "next big thing." Already the secondary market for *Attic Treasures* has developed along the same patterns as *Beanie Babies*, with different generations of swing tags being an important factor in determining values.

That now-famous Ty heart-shaped swing tag has become quite an appealing sight for plush lovers. Many collectors are also turning to the lovable *Pillow Pals* and *Ty Plush* animals. Some of Ty's animals were produced long before the *Beanie Babies* craze, so finding old *Ty Plush* pieces with mint condition tags is a rare treat!

WHERE TO SHOP

Once you've learned about what the secondary market entails, you may be wondering how to get there. There are a wealth of options. Your first step may be to contact your local retailer. While most retailers do not deal in the secondary market themselves, they may be able to supply a variety of sources that do, or offer some good advice on where else to turn. Also, your retailer may be the host of a swap-and-sell in your area where you may find other collectors looking to buy, sell or trade pieces. Another method for procuring hard-to-find Ty plush animals is through the classified sections of newspapers and collectors' magazines, although this method is a bit slower and may require some patience.

Perhaps the easiest and most effective method to utilizing the secondary market is through the Internet. By accessing any of the number of search engines available, you will be amazed at the amount of sites devoted to Ty. On-line, there will be a wealth of information at your fingertips, including breaking news and gossip. The

ATTIC TREASURES™ SECONDARY MARKET TIP

Shop According To Swing Tags Rather Than Clothes. There's a temptation to assume that an *Attic Treasures* piece without clothes is an older version. Because articles of clothing can easily be removed, it's best to examine the swing tag to determine the approximate age of the piece.

Internet may also provide many great opportunities to buy, sell and trade collectibles. There are lots of great sites and bulletin boards dedicated to such action, not to mention "cyber auctions," where you'll be able buy and sell for a small fee. Remember, however, that caution is key to successful Internet dealings. Always take your time and shop around for the best price and be sure to check the references of anyone you'll be doing business with.

SHOULD YOU JOIN THE RACE FOR TY® COLLECTIBLES?

Many new collectors see the "craziness" of the Ty plush animal phenomenon and wonder if they should avoid getting caught up in it. The best way to enjoy collecting is to stay informed, set goals and be patient. Identify the plush animals that you really like, set up a budget that you can truly afford, shop around for retailers or secondary market dealers that you can trust and acquire the plush animals when they become available at a price you believe is fair.

While the secondary market is a great way to add to your collection, always remember that, like the stock market, there is no guarantee on returns on your investment. The secondary market is volatile and changes occur daily, if not by the minute. Therefore, Ty plush animals are best collected for the joy that they were intended to bring, not for financial gain. As the years go by, you will always be able to look at your plush animal collection and smile because they are full of value – the sentimental kind!

*E*veryone needs a change every once in a while and the members of the Ty plush animal family are no exception. In the world of collectibles, when a piece undergoes a change, this change is known as a variation. Some of these changes are obvious while others are a bit more subtle. Most changes aren't officially announced, but are often discovered by observant collectors. Only some of them actually create a high demand for the piece and high value on the secondary market. While it is nearly impossible to determine which variations will soar in value, there are some specific changes that will more than likely command that higher value.

CLOTHING CHANGES

What to wear is always a tough decision and over the years, many Ty plush animals have undergone a change in wardrobe. This variation is most common among the *Attic Treasures* who, in the earlier years, appeared either without clothes, or with only a neck ribbon. More recently, they have become fashion-conscious and put on some pretty spiffy outfits, catapulting these older pieces into the realm of the variation. In some rare cases, such as with "Checkers," the animal decided that the "au naturel" look was more the way to go and, after donning clothes, recently took them off.

The *Attic Treasures* "Emily" experienced three changes in her dress. In 1994, when she was first introduced, "Emily" had only a ribbon around her neck. Then, a year later, in 1995, she showed up with a head bow instead. Finally, in 1996, "Emily" was completely decked out in a floral dress and matching bonnet.

A more subtle clothing change which occurs in

the *Attic Treasures*, *Pillow Pals* and *Ty Plush* lines is when the ribbon around the animal's neck changes color over the animal's years of production. This change doesn't typically affect the secondary market value of a piece. There are, however, a few exceptions, including the three color changes (red to green to navy) that the ribbon on the *Attic Treasures* bear "Reggie" underwent.

At this time, the increased secondary market value of this type of variation may be deceiving. While the animals wearing no clothes sometimes command a higher secondary market value, this occurrence is more likely a result of these designs being among the first produced (see *Swing Tags* section on 195 for additional information), rather than the fact that they're undressed.

COLOR CHANGES

Another obvious change that occurs among the animals is a change in color. Sometimes, as is the case with the *Pillow Pals* piece "Meow," the entire body of the animal changes color. First introduced as a gray cat in early 1997, this fluffy feline began its second of its nine lives later that same year as a cream Siamese cat with bright blue eyes and brown paws, ears and nose.

Another dramatic example of a color change has occurred in a few of the *Attic Treasures* pieces. "Pouncer," who made his debut in 1994 as an all gold cat, started appearing in 1995 with a white muzzle, a white-tipped tail and one white ear.

DESIGN CHANGES

Probably the most obvious, and often confusing, of the variations is the design change. With this type of variation, the name and the style number of the animal remain the same, but the piece looks completely different. There are several different ways in which this type of variation occurs, some of which are much more apparent than others.

Among the most well-known of the design change variations are the "old face" and "new face" *Beanie Babies* teddies. In January 1995, these teddies reappeared with a whole new look – one that has been mirrored in most *Beanie Babies* bears since. At first, the teddies appeared with a pointed snout and with their eyes far apart, while in later versions their faces appeared more rounded, as well as significantly larger. As a result, their older-style faces became a coveted commodity on the secondary market.

"Peter," a *Ty Plush* rabbit, is another example of a very extreme alteration in design. When he was first introduced in 1989, "Peter" was not jointed and was very "cartoonish" in appearance. In 1996, he lost his baby face and became much more realistic in appearance with changes to his body (he was now jointed), face and ears.

Similar to "Peter" the rabbit's change in body style, many *Ty Plush* animals have had style changes that have affected the structure of their bodies. Several *Ty Plush* pieces originally appeared in stores with a rigid body that held the animal to one position, usually either sitting or standing. Later on, perhaps in an attempt to provide the creatures with a more "cuddly" appearance, many of these animals were "under-stuffed," allowing the owner to position the animal in a variety of poses. "Spout" the elephant is a perfect example of this type of design change as he changed from sitting to "under-stuffed" (often called "floppy") in 1998.

Other design changes are not as obvious, but are quite notable. For example, the *Ty Plush* chick "Peepers" put on a pair of feet between 1991 and 1992. "Emily" from *Attic Treasures* lost a few shoe sizes when her feet shrank in 1994 and her cousin "Clifford" was originally produced with a humpback. Also, the *Ty Plush* "Al E. Kat" changed his body position in 1992 as he decided that he was much more comfortable curling up.

FABRIC CHANGES

A fabric change occurs when the material used to produce the animal changes. This alteration may be as dramatic as a change in the fabric of the entire piece, or as subtle as a change in the fabric of a small detail such as whiskers or antennas.

"Lucky" the ladybug member of the *Beanie Babies* underwent a change in her fabric. When she was first introduced in the summer of 1994, her spots were felt and they were glued to her shell. In 1996, after realizing the extra material was weighing her down in flight, she changed her look and her spots became part of the fabric from which she was made.

Many times, changes in fabric will provide for slight variations in a piece. A new batch of fabric used by Ty may result in subtle differences in either color or texture. Consequently, the same animal produced at different times may appear in a different shade, such as "Patti" the *Beanie Babies* platypus, or may appear to have "fuller hair" or more or less curls. Other than the platypus' dramatic metamorphosis, these variations are not often sought after by collectors.

NAME CHANGES

Sometimes animals go through a bit of an identity crisis, and a few of the animals in the Ty line have undergone a name change as a result.

One of the more valuable variations of this type is the *Beanie Babies* bear named "Brownie." Introduced in 1994, "Brownie" changed his name that same year, for an unknown reason, to "Cubbie." Today, "Brownie," although identical to "Cubbie" in every way but his name, is one of the most esteemed (and valuable) members of the *Beanie Babies* family.

SIZE CHANGES

Collectors often consider their plush animals to be like their very own children, and sometimes they get to see these critters grow up. For example, over one year of production, the *Ty Plush* piece "Sugar" actually had a growth spurt of six inches.

While this type of variation does not command a significantly higher value on the secondary market, it is a notable change, and of great interest to collectors.

STITCHING CHANGES

Stitching changes are a much more subtle variation that may go unnoticed by many collectors, However, in many instances, this variation commands a higher value on the secondary market. Stitching changes can include the color of thread used as well as the actual design of the stitching.

For example, the thread used on the wings of "Magic" the *Beanie Babies* dragon was changed from its original pale pink to hot pink in mid-1996. However, in

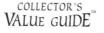

early 1997, "Magic" decided that the flashy tone was not the right one for her and the stitching was again changed to a pale pink hue.

TAG ERRORS

A tag error is one of the variations that may cause certain animals' secondary market values to sky-rocket, as was the case when "Punchers," the alter-ego of "Pinchers," made its way to the secondary market. With this type of variation, the actual animal is the same as its counterpart, but the tag information is different. In these cases, a word may be spelled incorrectly (often found in *Beanie Babies* poems), some of the printed information may be incorrect or, in more dramatic cases, the tag may actually belong to another animal or the name of the animal may be wrong altogether.

The Beanie Babies Collection
Pinchers ™ style 4026
© 1993 Ty Inc. Oakbrook, IL. USA
All Rights Reserved. Caution:
Remove this tag before giving
toy to a child. For ages 5 and up.
Handmade in Korea.
Surface
Wash.

The Beanie Babies Collection
Punchers ™ style 4026
© 1993 Ty Inc. Oakbrook, IL. USA
All Rights Reserved. Caution:
Remove this tag before giving
toy to a child. For ages 5 and up.
Handmade in Korea.
Surface
Wash.

"Baby Spice" from *Ty Plush* is a good example of this type of variation. On some pieces, the baby bear's swing tag was correct. However, the name of the bear on some of the tags was mistyped and actually read "ByBy Spice."

While some of these variations prove to be rare finds and are valuable on the secondary market, this is not always the case. However, just knowing that these variations exist can be of great interest to collectors and can make the world of collecting even more of a challenge and a whole lot of fun!

*T*he heart-shaped design of the Ty swing tag is what distinguishes Ty plush animals from all of the others on a gift shop shelf. However long before *Beanie Babies* made Ty a household word, the swing tags on new purchases were removed from the animal's ear as a safety measure – if the animal was for a child – or just because the stiff paper tag was considered a nuisance when hugging the new friend. Today, collectors are becoming more aware of the importance of these tags, especially when dealing with the secondary market. This is especially true for the *Attic Treasures* and *Beanie Babies* markets – and who knows what the future holds for the tags on the other Ty plush animals.

> ### THE PRICE IS RIGHT BUT THE PRICE TAG IS NOT
>
> A retail price tag which is still glued to the swing tag may decrease the value of your piece. However, some collectors view these price tags as another source of information regarding point of purchase and original cost.

The condition of the piece is of primary concern when buying or selling on the secondary market. This applies not only to the general overall appearance of the piece itself but also to the condition and presence of the tags. Tags play an important role in the world of collecting. For one thing, they indicate the authenticity of the piece. They also help to define the age of the piece, as throughout the years of a line's production, the tag may undergo many changes. The early tag versions are the most rare and sought after since the animals sporting these tags were among the first of that particular design produced.

ATTIC TREASURES™ SWING TAGS

Generation 1: These tags are single red hearts with no fold and have a skinny "ty" printed on front. Both the word and the tag itself are outlined in gold. The reverse side lists the name, style number, designer name (if applicable), company information and care and cautionary notes.

The Attic Treasures Collection
Emily ™ - Style 6016
© 1992 Ty Inc. Oakbrook, IL USA
Designed by Nola Hart
All Rights Reserved Caution
Remove this tag before giving
toy to a child. For ages 5 and up.
Printed in Korea
Handmade in China
Surface
Wash

Generation 2: The front of this tag is identical to its predecessor, but the folded heart opens like a book. The left side displays company information and care instructions while the right side displays the animal's name and style number as well as a "to/from/with love" section for gift giving. On the back, the UPC (Universal Product Code) information is printed with the phrase "Retain Tag For Reference."

The Attic Treasures Collection
© 1993 Ty Inc. Oakbrook IL. USA
All Rights Reserved. Caution:
Remove this tag before giving
toy to a child. For ages 3 and up.
Handmade in China
Surface
Wash.

Cassie ™ style 6028
to
from
with
love

Generation 3: Used for only a brief period, the only design change in this tag is the bigger font size used to print the Ty letters on the swing tag's front. The two letters are "puffed out," resembling the familiar Ty logo used today.

The Attic Treasures Collection
© 1993 Ty Inc. Oakbrook IL. USA
All Rights Reserved. Caution:
Remove this tag before giving
toy to a child. For ages 3 and up.
Handmade in China
Surface
Wash.

Emily ™ style 6018
to
from
with
love

Generation 4: These tags are identical in design to the Generation 3 tags except for the diagonal green stripe with the word "collectible" which is added to the upper right hand corner. Inside on the left, Ty production locations are added and the care and cautionary recommendations are moved to the back. In addition to these changes, the printed name of the collection reads "Ty Collectibles™."

COLLECTIBLE

Ty Collectibles ™
©Ty Inc.
Oakbrook IL. U.S.A.
Ty UK Ltd.
Waterlooville, Hants
P08 9HH
Ty Deutschland
90008 Nürnberg
Handmade in China

Jeremy ™ style 6008
to
from
with
love

Generation 5: This design is dramatically different from the red heart tag of other Ty products. The front is beige with tiny brown paw prints in the background while the Ty logo and the diagonal banner which reads "collectible" has changed to burgundy. The information on the inside remains the same as previous generation tags, but an additional warning is added on the back of the tag with the title "Safety Precaution" as well as the specific advice to remove "all tags, buttons, and other accessories before giving to a child under 3 years of age."

Ty Collectibles ™

© Ty Inc.
Oakbrook IL. U.S.A.

© Ty UK Ltd.
Fareham, Hants
PO15 5TX

© Ty Deutschland
90008 Nürnberg
Handmade in China

Mason ™ style 6020
Designed by Ruth E. Fraser

to _____
from _____
with
love

Generation 6: The front of the latest design looks exactly like the Generation 5 tag. On the inside, the collection's name is once again "The Attic Treasures Collection™," and the style number has been deleted (this information can be found on the back of the tag as the last four numbers of the UPC bar code). Also, the word "button" no longer appears in the "Safety Precaution" text.

The Attic Treasures Collection™

© Ty Inc.
Oakbrook. IL. U.S.A

© Ty Europe Ltd.
Fareham. Hants
PO15 5TX U.K.

© Ty Canada
Aurora. Ontario
Handmade in China

Piccadilly ™

to _____
from _____
with
love

BEANIE BABIES® SWING TAGS

Generation 1 (Early 1994-Mid 1994): These tags are single red hearts with no fold and have a skinny "ty" printed on front. The animal's name, style number, reference to "The Beanie Babies Collection" and company information all appear on the back.

The Beanie Babies Collection
Brownie ™ style 4010
© 1993 Ty Inc. Oakbrook, IL. USA
All Rights Reserved. Caution:
Remove this tag before giving
toy to a child. For ages 5 and up.
Handmade in Korea.
Surface
Wash.

Generation 2 (Mid 1994-Early 1995): The front of this tag features the same skinny "ty" logo and red heart design, but the tag opens like a book. Inside is the name and style number, a "to/from/with love" section for gift giving, reference to "The

The Beanie Babies Collection
© 1993 Ty Inc. Oakbrook IL. USA
All Rights Reserved. Caution:
Remove this tag before giving
toy to a child. For ages 3 and up.
Handmade in China
Surface
Wash.

Chilly ™ style 4012

to _____
from _____
with
love

Beanie Babies Collection," plus care, cautionary and company information.

Generation 3 (Early 1995-Early 1996):
This tag is the first to feature the "puffed out" Ty logo. Inside, the information remains the same except for the addition of a trademark symbol after the word "Babies" in the collection's name and Ty's three corporate addresses.

Generation 4 (Early 1996-Late 1997):
The addition of a yellow star emblazoned with the words "Original Beanie Baby" make this swing tag quite distinct from its predecessors. The inside of the swing tag also underwent a dramatic change with the addition of the animal's birthday and poem, as well as Ty's web site address.

Generation 5 (Late 1997-Current):
The outside of this tag is similar to the 4th generation tag, with the only difference being the typeface of "Original Beanie Baby." On the inside, the animal's birthday is written out (February 13, 1995 instead of 2-13-95), the Internet address is abbreviated and the piece's style number deleted (this information can be found as the last four digits of the UPC bar code on the back of the tag). The corporate offices of Ty UK and Ty Deutschland became collectively known as "Ty Europe" and were listed alongside Ty USA and Ty Canada. Also, the name "Beanie Babies Collection" became registered (®).

TEENIE BEANIE BABIES™ SWING TAGS

1997 Version: The *Teenie Beanie Babies* released during the first promotion feature single red heart tags with no fold. The Ty logo features "puffed out" lettering and the tag has a gold outline. On the back of the tag, the name of the collection, the animal's name and company information appears. Also, next to the collection and animal names, the trademark symbol reads "TM/MC."

1998 Version: The 1998 swing tag version features the same front as 1997. On the back of the tag, the typeface is different, the web site address is added and the trademark symbols read "TM/MC/MR." Because two different companies produced the 1998 *Teenie Beanie Babies*, there are subtle spacing differences on these swing tags.

PILLOW PALS™ SWING TAGS

Originally, *Pillow Pals* swing tags were much larger than the ones the critters wear today, although the outside design mirrors the more recent ones with their "puffed out" Ty logo and gold lining. Inside information on early tags includes the collection name, company information, the animal's name and style number and a "to/from/with love" section for gift giving.

The tags eventually switched to a smaller size – the same size as *Beanie Babies* tags – and Ty's office locations were added to the company information. This version was modified again with a change in the typeface and the deletion of the design's style number.

Another swing tag change of interest to *Pillow Pals* collectors is the addition of prayer poems instead of the gift giving section on the inside of the tags for the May 1998 releases ("Paddles" and "Sherbet"). As of this printing, the other current *Pillow Pals* had yet to appear with prayer poems on their swing tags.

TY® PLUSH SWING TAGS

The first *Ty Plush* tag from 1986 is a red, hard plastic heart tag, attached around the animal's neck. Immediately recognized as a choking hazard, this tag was discontinued.

There are several versions of the paper swing tags found on later *Ty Plush* animals: one features a plain red heart with the letters "ty." while others have the words "BEAN BAG" in red letters on a banner in the upper right-hand corner.

Other *Ty Plush* animals feature tags with "ty" appearing horizontally on the red tag, with the letters "t" and "y" used as the first letters for the words "to" and "you," followed by " . . . with love." Some of these tags also feature "BEAN BAG" on a diagonal yellow banner.

A later tag design features the original Ty logo standing alone, this time with a black border around the letters. The current swing tag design features a larger, "puffed out" Ty logo and comes in two different sizes, depending on the size of the animal to which it is attached.

*T*he cloth body tags that are sewn into the seam found on the bottom or "tush" of Ty plush animals have also gone through design changes which are designated by different "versions." The information found on the tush tags can be somewhat helpful in determining the approximate age of the item, but this strategy is not always accurate. For example, an *Attic Treasures* animal released in 1998 can sit on a tush tag dated 1993!

ATTIC TREASURES™ TUSH TAGS

When *Attic Treasures* was introduced in 1993, the tags were white with black printing and had no Ty logo. In a later tag design, the Ty heart was added to the white tag and the printing was in red. The current tush tag has a burgundy background with cream lettering.

BEANIE BABIES® TUSH TAGS

Version 1: The first *Beanie Babies* tush tags are white with black printing and list company and production information.

Version 1

Version 2: The red heart Ty logo is added to the information on the tush tag which is printed in red.

Version 3: This tag features the addition of the name of the animal below the Ty heart and "The Beanie Babies Collection™" above.

Version 2   **Version 3**

Version 4: This tush tag sports a small red star in the upper left-hand side of the Ty heart logo. On some tags, a clear sticker with the star was placed next to the Ty logo.

Version 5: In late 1997, these tags began to appear with a registration mark (®) after "Beanie Babies" in the collection's name and a trademark (™) after the animal's name.

Version 4   **Version 5**

Version 6

Version 6: The most recent tush tags feature another slight change in trademark symbols. The registration mark (®) in the collection's name moved from after "Beanie Babies" to after "Collection," replacing the previous trademark. Some of the recent tush tags have also noted a change to "P.E." pellets rather than "P.V.C."

TEENIE BEANIE BABIES™ TUSH TAGS

These tags feature the familiar red heart as well as the copyright, company and production information, printed in red. On the reverse side, printed in black, is content and manufacturing information.

PILLOW PALS™ TUSH TAGS

The first of these tags were white with the Ty logo heart on one side. On the reverse side was the production information and care and age recommendations. The only change that the tags have undergone is the elimination of the age recommendation and the addition of the "CE" symbol.

TY® PLUSH TUSH TAGS

Through the years, *Ty Plush* animals have appeared with a number of different tush tags. A unique early tush tag featured a cream satin tag with a red heart outline around the familiar Ty logo written in black. Recent animals feature white tush tags with a red Ty heart logo on the front. On the back, "Ty, Inc." and the copyright year appear in red type, followed by company and production information in dark brown or black type. Differences on various tags include the kinds of pellets (P.V.C. or P.E.), the country where it was produced (China or Korea), as well as other slight variances.

*T*here's a lot of sentimental value, as well as monetary value, to attribute to your Ty plush animal collection and now that you've built it, it's time to think about protecting it.

Today, there are many items on the market designed specifically to help you protect your valuable plush pieces. Once just a novelty, acrylic tag protectors have become almost as common as the Ty tags themselves. Because the secondary market places a great deal of importance on the condition of the swing tags, value-conscious collectors have rushed to protect their tags! A clear acrylic snap-on (whether hard or soft) will keep your tag in perfect condition. There are also soft poly "sleeves" that slip on over the tag. To protect the plush animal itself, specially-designed acrylic containers and boxes have become a popular storage option. These products, while easy-to-use and inexpensive, can prove to be extremely valuable additions to your collection.

As Ty plush animals were intended to be well-loved, you might find that every once in a while they are in need of a bath. Most of the *Beanie Babies* and *Pillow Pals* are washable. Those that can't be washed are the ones with felt or glued-on features. If you wash your animal, remove its swing tag first, then place the animal in a pillowcase for extra protection. Be sure to use mild detergent and wash on the gentle cycle. To dry, use a hair dryer or let air dry.

Ty Plush and *Attic Treasures* can only be surface washed because of their delicate hair and texture. Simply use a damp wash cloth dipped in mild detergent and gently rub the dirty area. Be sure to first test on an inconspicuous area for color fading.

Sometimes a bath isn't enough to remove odors such

as smoke which have settled into an animal's fur. If such an odor is present, place the animal in an airtight plastic bag with an open box of baking soda. After about a day, the odor should no longer be present. On the secondary market, many discerning shoppers will look for "smoke-free" plush animals.

Even though you have done everything in your power to ensure that your collection remains in the best possible condition, there are some circumstances that may occur beyond your control. Therefore, it is a good idea to look into insuring your collection. Most renters and homeowners insurance policies cover collectibles, but to insure your collection for a specific dollar amount, ask your agent about adding a Personal Articles Floater or a Fine Arts Floater, or "rider," to your policy. You may also insure your collection under a sperate policy all together.

> Many companies will accept a reputable secondary market price guide - such as the Collector's Value Guide™ - as a valid source for determining your collection's value.

In the event of a loss, you will need a record of the contents and value of your collection. Ask your insurance agent what information is acceptable. Keep receipts and an inventory of your collection in a different location, such as a safe-deposit box. Include the purchase date, price paid, size, issue year, tag generation information (if applicable) and secondary market value for each piece. Photographs are also good backups.

In determining the type of coverage you'll need, calculate how much it would cost to replace your collection and compare it to the total amount your policy would pay. Weigh the options of losing – and trying to replace – your collection, against the cost you'll pay for insuring it, just in case.

*H*ow well do you know the entire Ty plush animal collection – *Attic Treasures*, *Beanie Babies*, *Teenie Beanie Babies*, *Pillow Pals* and *Ty Plush* animals? You can find out by taking our quiz and then checking your answers at the bottom of the page.

1. Which two *Beanie Babies* are not animals?

2. Which two *Pillow Pals* have been released with prayer poems printed on their tags?

3. Name the *Beanie Babies* animal that is holding something between its paws.

4. Name the three teddy bear artists from Canada who were given credit for designing selected *Attic Treasures* pieces.

5. What size are the largest *Ty Plush* bears?

6. Name two *Beanie Babies* that have their teeth showing.

7. In mid-1996, most of the members of *Attic Treasures* underwent a common change. What was this?

8. How many hippos have been issued in the Ty plush animals family and what are their names?

9. To date, there have only been seven *Pillow Pals* removed from production. Name them.

10. There is a highly unusual and magical piece in the *Ty Plush* "Country" collection. What is it?

1. "Spooky" the ghost and "Snowball" the snowman 2. "Sherbet" and "Paddles." 3. "Seaweed" 4. Linda Harris, Ruth Fraser and Nola Hart 5. 50 inches ("Papa PJ", "Papa Pumpkin", "Papa Rumples" and "Papa Shaggy") 6. "Bucky" the beaver and "Crunch" the shark 7. They got dressed 8. "Grace" (*Attic Treasures*), "Happy" (*Beanie Babies*), "Happy" (*Teenie Beanie Babies*), "Tubby" (*Beanie Babies*), "Huggy," "Purr," "Ribbit" (#3006), "Snap," (#3007), "Snap" (#3015), "Snuggy," "Zulu," "Nuts" 10. "Sparkles," the unicorn

CE — mark imprinted on tush tags of recent Ty plush animals, indicating the pieces were manufactured according to consumer safety regulations.

collectible — anything and everything that is "able to be collected," such as figurines and dolls. Even *seashells* can be considered a "collectible," but it is generally recognized that a true collectible should be something that increases in value over time.

current — piece that is in current production, although it may not be readily available in retail stores.

exchange — secondary market service that lists pieces that collectors wish to buy or sell. The exchange works as a middleman and usually requires a commission.

issue price — retail price of an item when it is first introduced.

issue year — the year that the piece becomes available in the general collection.

limited edition (LE) — piece scheduled for a predetermined production quantity or time.

markings — any of the various identifying features found on a collectible. This can be information found on tush tags or swing tags, such as an artist's signature.

members only piece — the piece that is available for purchase only by members of the Beanie Babies Official Club. In 1998, the members only piece was "Clubby."

mint condition — piece offered on the secondary market that is in like-new condition.

mint condition with both tags (MWBT) — piece offered on the secondary market in like-new condition with pristine swing tag and tush tag attached.

mint in bag (MIB) — on the secondary market, term for *Teenie Beanie Babies* in like-new condition in the original, unopened plastic bag.

mistags — errors in swing tags and tush tags, including mismatched tags and misspellings. Because Ty plush animals are mass produced, tag errors are common and rarely affect a piece's value on the secondary market.

new release — new piece in the collection announced during the year. For Ty plush animals, there are usually two or three major introductions per year, as well as special announcements for single items, such as "Princess."

open edition — piece with no pre-determined limitation on time or size of production run.

P.E. pellets — small, round plastic polyethylene "beans" used as weighted fillings in many Ty plush animals.

primary market — conventional collectibles purchasing process in which collectors buy directly from dealers at issue price.

P.V.C. pellets — small, round plastic polyvinyl chloride "beans" used as weighted fillings in many Ty plush animals.

retired — piece that is taken out of production, never to be made again. This is usually followed by a scarcity of the piece and an increase in value on the secondary market (also see *secondary market*).

secondary market — source for buying and selling collectibles according to basic supply-and-demand principles ("pay what the market will bear"). Popular pieces that are sold out or have been retired can appreciate in value far above the original issue price. Pieces are sold through newspaper ads, collector newsletters, the Internet and "swap & sells" at collector gatherings.

swap & sell — event where collectors meet to buy, sell or trade items.

swing tag — heart-shaped paper tag that comes attached to each Ty plush animal. This tag is attached by a small plastic strip, and is usually attached to the animal's left ear or head area.

tag generations — style changes in the swing tags, which can help determine the ages of Ty plush animals.

tush tag — folded fabric tag sewn into the seam near the bottom of the Ty plush animal (*note: Teenie Beanie Babies do not have folded tags*).

variations — items that have color, design or printed text changes from the "original" pieces, whether intentional or not. Some of these changes are minor, while some are important enough to affect the value of a piece on the secondary market.

INDEX BY ANIMAL TYPE

– Key –

All Ty plush animals are listed below in order by animal types. The first number refers to the piece's location (Page #) in the book and the second number refers to the box (Pict. #) in which it is pictured on that page.

Attic Treasures™ — (AT)
Beanie Babies® — (BB)
Teenie Beanie Babies™ — (TB)
Pillow Pals™ — (PP)
Ty® Plush — (PL)

	Page #	Pict #
ALLIGATOR		
Ally™ (BB)	63	2
ANTEATER		
Ants™ (BB)	63	3
ARMADILLO		
Tank™ (BB)	89	132
BATS		
Batty™ (BB)	63	5
Radar™ (BB)	82	97
BEARS		
1991 Ty Collectable Bear™ (PL)	108	1
1992 Ty Collectable Bear™ (PL)	108	2
1997 Holiday Bear™ (PL)	108	3
1997 Teddy™ (BB)	62	1
Abby™ (AT)	43	1
Arctic™ (PL)	168	291
Aurora™ (PL)	109	4
Baby Buddy™ (PL)	109	5
Baby Cinnamon™ (PL)	109	6
Baby Curly™ (PL, #5017)	109	7
Baby Curly™ (PL, #5018)	109	8
Baby Ginger™ (PL)	110	9
Baby Paws™ (PL, #5110)	110	10
Baby Paws™ (PL, #5111)	110	11
Baby Paws™ (PL, #5112)	110	12
Baby PJ™ (PL, #5016)	110	13
Baby PJ™ (PL, #5100)	111	14
Baby Powder™ (PL)	111	15
Baby Spice™ (PL)	111	16
Bailey™ (PL)	111	17
Bamboo™ (PL, #5106)	111	18

BEARS, cont.	Page #	Pict #
Bamboo™ (PL, #5113)	112	19
Baron™ (PL)	112	20
Barry™ (AT)	43	3
Beanie Bear™ (PL, #5000)	112	21
Beanie Bear™ (PL, #5100)	112	22
Beanie Bear™ (PL, #5101)	112	23
Beanie Bear™ (PL, #5102)	113	24
Bearington™ (AT)	44	4
Big Beanie Bear™ (PL, #5011)	113	25
Big Beanie Bear™ (PL, #5200)	113	26
Big Beanie Bear™ (PL, #5201)	113	27
Big Beanie Bear™ (PL, #5202)	113	28
Big Pudgy™ (PL)	114	29
Big Shaggy™ (PL)	114	30
Blackie™ (BB)	64	8
Blackie™ (PL)	114	31
Bluebeary™ (AT)	44	7
Boris™ (AT)	45	9
Britannia™ (BB)	65	12
Brownie™ (BB)	65	14
Brownie™ (PL)	114	32
Buddy™ (PL, #5007)	114	33
Buddy™ (PL, #5019)	115	34
ByBy Spice™ (PL)	111	16
Carlton™ (AT)	45	11
Casanova™ (AT)	45	12
Cassie™ (AT)	45	13
Charles™ (AT)	46	14
Checkers™ (AT)	46	15
Chelsea™ (AT)	46	16
Chilly™ (BB)	66	20
Christopher™ (AT)	46	17
Cinnamon™ (PL, #5004)	115	35
Cinnamon™ (PL, #5021)	115	36
Clifford™ (AT)	46	18
Clubby™ (BB)	67	25
Clyde™ (AT)	47	19
Cocoa™ (PL)	115	37
Cody™ (AT)	47	20
Copperfield™ (AT)	47	22
Cubbie™ (BB)	68	29
Curly™ (BB)	68	30
Curly™ (PL, #5300)	116	38
Curly™ (PL, #5301)	116	39
Curly™ (PL, #5302)	116	40
Cuzzy™ (PL)	116	41
Dexter™ (AT)	47	23

INDEX BY ANIMAL TYPE

Index By Animal Type

– Key –

All Ty plush animals are listed below in alphabetical order. Use the check box to indicate what you have. The first number refers to the piece's location (Page #) in the book and the second number refers to the box (Pict. #) in which it is pictured on that page.

Attic Treasures™ — (AT)
Beanie Babies® — (BB)
Teenie Beanie Babies™ — (TB)
Pillow Pals™ — (PP)
Ty® Plush — (PL)

ALPHABETICAL INDEX

ALPHABETICAL INDEX

ACKNOWLEDGEMENTS

Collectors' Publishing would like to thank Paul Dennen, Ellen Hearst, Mr. and Mrs. D. Howard, Wendy Murray, Jennifer Smolin and Michele Smolin and the many other people who contributed their valuable time to assist us with this book.

Look for these other

COLLECTOR'S ™
VALUE GUIDE

titles at fine gift and collectible stores everywhere.

Department 56®
Villages

Department 56®
Snowbabies™

HALLMARK
Keepsake Ornaments

SWAROVSKI
Silver Crystal

Cherished
Teddies®
by ENESCO ®

Ty® Plush
Animals

Ty® Beanie Babies®

COLLECTORS'
PUBLISHING

598 Pomeroy Ave., Meriden, CT 06450
www.collectorspub.com